ENGLISH

ENGLISH PAPER MONEY

Vincent Duggleby

SPINK
London

First published 1975
Second edition 1980
Third edition 1984
Fourth edition 1990

British Library Cataloguing in Publication Data
Duggleby, Vincent
   English paper money—4th ed.
   1. English banknotes—Collectors' guides
   I. Title
   769.55942

ISBN 0–907605–31–1

Published by Spink & Son Limited, London SW1Y 6QS
© Vincent Duggleby 1990

Typeset and printed by Pardy & Son (Printers) Ltd., Ringwood

Contents

Preface to the Fourth Edition

On 7 June 1990, the Bank of England issued the first of the new series E notes, the £5. It features the railway engineer George Stephenson and over the next three or four years new designs for the £10, £20 and £50 will appear.

Designing banknotes is a very long and painstaking process and work on the series E has been going on since 1985. Indeed it is 20 years since the first of the existing series D notes, the £20, was issued, just about the time that I first began my research into the field of *English Paper Money* and it is five years since the third edition was published.

Much has happened in that period including the end of the £1 note which was marked by considerable publicity in the newspapers and a competition in the Daily Telegraph to find the highest numbered note in the last prefix of the series (DY21). Although the Bank of England stopped issuing them at the end of 1984, £1 notes retained their legal tender status until 11 March 1988, and can always be exchanged at the Bank's head office in Threadneedle Street.

Just a few days earlier, on 1 March 1988, a new Chief Cashier, Mr. Malcolm Gill, took over from Mr. David Somerset who had been in office since March 1980. The pace of technological change and the increasing sophistication of colour photocopies meant that the Pictorial series D notes underwent several important security changes, notably the introduction of the windowed or stardust thread, which is being carried over to the new series. It is perhaps worth recalling that it is exactly 50 years since a security thread was first used by the Bank at the outset of the Second World War.

In 1987 the Bank made available unique items from its archives for a major exhibition at the British Museum "As Good As Gold: 300 years of British Bank Note Design" and a book of that title was published. One of the authors, John Keyworth, is Curator of the Bank's museum which was opened to the general public in November 1988 and provides a fascinating insight into the development of paper currency over 300 years.

The launch of the series E notes has been marked by the Bank taking a more positive approach to the needs of collectors who are no longer regarded as the oddballs they once were. Indeed a wholly-owned subsidary, Debden Security Printing has been set up in response to genuine public interest and curiosity about the Bank's present and past work.

Various items are being made available, including a limited edition of framed pairs of the last series D and first series E £5 notes; notes encased in acrylic for use as ornamental paperweights; and a 32-page booklet "The New £5 note and George Stephenson". As the Bank approaches its tercentenary in 1994, other ideas are under discussion—how about a limited edition of the white fiver? That would be a marvellous memento.

Detailed classification of the Series E notes will have to await the next edition but in the meantime all prefix codes of existing notes are listed in this catalogue and the new collector will find additional information at the end in the Appendices, with hints for beginners and a completely revised section on the old white high denomination notes. Changes in the numbering have been kept to a minimum but inevitably the Somerset section has had to be revised to take account of the various new issues. I am also pleased for the first time to be able to include photographs of all the Chief Cashiers from Patrick Mahon to Malcolm Gill.

Prices in general show a marked increase for earlier issues and for rare prefixes as demand outstrips supply and the discovery of a fresh hoard becomes a less frequent occurrence (the sale in 1989 of more than 100 pre first world war Nairne high denomination notes was perhaps the most exciting event for serious collectors). But it is always worthwhile keeping in touch with your local bank manager in case some old notes are returned.

I must apologise in advance for any errors, inconsistencies and omissions. Collectors are assiduous in their search for new information and, subject to limitations of space and format, I have adopted as much of this as possible.

Welcome to the fascinating world of English Paper Money!

Weybridge, July 1990   Vincent Duggleby

The Author

Vincent Duggleby is recognised as a leading authority on British Treasury and Bank of England notes of the twentieth century. His pioneering research has brought to light many aspects of note history and design—particularly during the First World War—which were previously unknown, and his widely used charts of the Bank of England prefix system are regarded as the standard reference.

Educated at Blundell's School, Devon, and at Worcester College, Oxford, he was Financial Editor of the B.B.C. until 1989 and is now a freelance broadcaster and financial journalist. The second edition of his book written with Louise Botting, "Making the Most of Your Money", was published in 1985.

He has been a member of the International Bank Note Society since 1969 and in 1990 was named the first winner of the Enid Salter Research Trophy. He is also Honorary Treasurer and a Fellow of the Royal Philatelic Society (specialising in the stamps of St. Vincent). In 1986 he was appointed to the Royal Mint Advisory Committee (under the Chairmanship of H.R.H. The Duke of Edinburgh).

Acknowledgements

The author has over the past 20 years of research into English Paper Money received help from more individuals and organisations than he could possibly hope to mention. Particular thanks for this edition are due to Barnaby Faull, head of Spinks' Banknote Department, David Keable (and the late Enid Salter whose death was a sad blow to all collectors), Bob Blake, Alistair Gibb, Michael O'Grady, Ernie Brooks and Lou Manzi.

And, of course, the Bank of England itself whose officials prefer to remain anonymous but who have given much guidance behind the scenes. The Bank owns the copyright of all its notes and permission to reproduce them is gratefully acknowledged.

Catalogue Terms

The technical term for the front of a banknote is the *obverse* and for the back of a note, the *reverse*.

The *Prefix coding* is the combination of letters and numbers that precede the actual serial number. For example: on a Treasury note or a white Bank of England note a typical prefix might be:

$\dfrac{B}{41}$ (= letter over number) $\dfrac{100}{H}$ (= number over letter)

Many Treasury notes also have 'dot' and 'dash' variations. This is the mark that appears under the 'No' and depending on the actual note may or may not make it more valuable.

On Bank of England notes you will find various prefix combinations such as:

X41 (= letter, number, number);   R31L (= letter, number, number, letter)

28A (= number, number, letter);   AN64 (= letter, letter, number, number)

Because banknote serials are made up of letters as well as numbers, the letters of the alphabet traced for a particular issue are listed.

The quantities printed represent the best estimate that can be made calculated from the range of serial prefixes traced. They are NOT official issue figures.

Bank of England notes since 1940 have incorporated a metal thread as an important safeguard against forgery.

This thread shows up clearly when the note is held up to the light and, in the case of the latest windowed, or stardust, version as it is known, it is clearly visible from the front of the note.

Because most modern notes are multicoloured, the catalogue gives only the predominant colours for each type.

All illustrations are approximately half linear size and in accordance with Bank of England guidelines (July 1989) photographs of notes issued after 1960 which contain a portrait of the Queen have been *overlaid* with the word SPECIMEN. These should not be confused with genuine specimen notes which are *overprinted* by the Bank.

Pricing

The notes have in most cases been priced for Extremely Fine (*EF*) and Very Fine (*VF*) examples. It is a matter of subjective judgement as to the precise definition and price of an uncirculated note, and what allowance, for example, should be made for the fact that it has been counted by a bank cashier. A dealer's price for a truly 100% uncirculated note will normally, but not invariably, be higher than the catalogue price for an EF example.

However, it must be said that many pre-Second World War prefixes are very rarely found in 100% UNC and the same is true of some scarce post war prefixes. Rather than complicate and confuse collectors by quoting too many price differentials which might be unsustainable, the author and the publishers feel that it is in everyone's best interest for the EF/VF system to be maintained. Collectors should also remember that dealers adjust prices in the light of the latest market conditions and take account of supply and demand.

From the first edition it has been the practice to quote a price for the whole of the first alphabetical prefix (often A) rather than the first numerical prefix (often A01). It should be borne in mind that these A01 notes (or the equivalent first issue where it has been clearly identified) may carry a substantial premium over and above the quoted price for first series generally.

However, in recognition of the fact that in the last few years a well-defined new issue market has developed, collectors will find prices quoted for the first run of notes from the Pictorial Series D onwards. The author and the publishers will keep under review the possibility of a similar approach to earlier issues provided they are satisfied a genuine market exists.

In some instances it has not been possible to quote any price. This is either because the note has not yet been traced or because there are too few examples in existence or, conversely, because the notes can be easily obtained from circulation at face value.

Before 1910 it becomes increasingly difficult to establish values simply because of rarity and because of differences in condition. The prices quoted should therefore be regarded as an indication of what dealers might offer or charge for the notes. It cannot be emphasised too strongly that the price of notes which the market judges to be scarce can change suddenly with the discovery of a fresh supply. At the end of the day a note is worth what someone will pay for it.

Treasury Notes 1914–1928

The outbreak of the First World War in August 1914 proved to be the end of Britain's "Golden Age" in more ways than one. Up until that time the gold sovereign and half sovereign had circulated as everyday currency for nearly a century even though the ordinary working man might never have handled them.

Following the 1833 Bank Charter Act, Bank of England notes were legal tender in England and Wales only for amounts of £5 and above. With the passing of the Currency and Bank Notes Act on 5 August 1914 (the day after war was declared) the Treasury was empowered to issue currency notes of £1 and 10s. with full legal tender status, with gold convertibility only indirectly through the Bank of England. The Bank had anticipated the likely restrictions on gold and had in fact already been working behind the scenes on a £1 of traditional design (see page 53) but it was rejected.

Instead H.M. Treasury, helped by the Inland Revenue, rushed through an emergency design during the weekend of 1/2 August and the notes were printed in round-the-clock shifts by Waterlow Bros. and Layton with help on the 10s. note by De La Rue. The Bank Holiday was extended for three days and during this time some four million £1 notes were produced.

Minutes in the Public Record Office give a graphic description of the wrangle between the Chancellor of the Exchequer, Lloyd George, and City bankers over the status of the new notes. Lloyd George was careful not to reveal his hand until it was virtually a *fait accompli*, and only conceded a major point on convertibility into gold on the grounds that without it the notes would certainly go to a discount.

The first Treasury notes were hurriedly and badly designed, and since there was no ready supply of banknote paper available (other than that held by the Bank of England) the printers had to use paper produced for postage stamps.

Recent research by Alistair Gibb (*Bond and Banknote News* No. 33 March/April 1989) has given a new and valuable insight into the production of the 1914 issue and in particular has drawn attention to the role of Sir Frederick Atterbury, Controller of H.M. Stationery Office. A letter from Lady Atterbury to a Sunday newspaper in 1933 recounted: "It may be of interest to your readers to know that on the Saturday before the eventful Bank Holiday of August 1914, Sir John Bradbury and a colleague came to my house at Hampstead Heath at night and asked my husband in the Chancellor's name, to get the paper money made ... it was a matter of extreme urgency and the first note was designed in my drawing room in a few minutes by my husband".

Lady Atterbury goes on to explain that Sir John Bradbury signed the notes "as it was not possible to obtain His Majesty's signature in the extreme haste required by Mr. Lloyd George", but this is most improbable. Following Bank of England precedent the notes had to be signed by someone and since they were currency notes issued by the Treasury it was logical to use a senior official on a par with the Bank's Chief Cashier. The choice fell on Bradbury as one of the two Permanent Secretaries and the notes quickly gained the nickname Bradburys, even though there might have been other suitable contenders.

Proofs of the first issue in various colours have now come to light indicating that black and red were not the automatic choice. The £1 was issued on Friday 7 August and the 10s. a week later.

It was only a matter of days before plans were put in hand to produce a more considered and permanent design. Despite strong and colourful competition from the various printers (Bradbury Wilkinson—no connection with Sir John—were particularly pressing), the contract for the second issue was again divided between De La Rue (£1 and 10s.) and Waterlow Bros. and Layton (10s. only). The designs were those of Mr. George Eve who also designed some of the George V postage stamps.

On 28 August 1914 they were approved by Lloyd George who had remarked during the second reading of the Currency and Banknotes Amendment Bill the previous day: "The new design will not compare in artistic merit with that of the Scottish banks. We had to consider a good many things and the first thing to consider in a note is whether it is easily forgeable or not. If you have a good mass of colour on your notes, it is not so easy to detect forgery. The simpler a design the more difficult it is to forge, just as the simpler a signature the more difficult it is to forge. Signatures with great flourishes are most easily forged. If you have a simple signature like that on the Bank of England note, it is the most difficult thing in the world for the forger. It is much more difficult to imitate simplicity than it is to imitate flourishes and special adornments. That is the principle on which we have proceeded in the preparation of these notes . . .".

A rather different view was taken (in private) by the Chairman of the Board of Inland Revenue, Sir Matthew Nathan, who said: "The design is not a good one. I preferred the school leaving certificate. But I think we shall get a clear well printed note with an easily seen and distinctive watermark making forgeries difficult. There will be no undue delay and the cost will not be excessive. When the public abuses the design we will take refuge in it having been made by H.M.'s designer of stamps".

The new £1 notes duly appeared on 23 October 1914 and the 10s. notes on 21 January 1915 without any noticeable complaints! It was, however, only a few months before discussions were under way on yet another change adopting many of the principles which had just been rejected. Preliminary work on the third issue Bradbury notes were undertaken by a designer known only as "Carlton" whose background and credentials remain a mystery. Unfortunately, there is a gap in the archives and the next we know is that in March 1916 Bertram Mackennal (designer of the coinage) had been 'good enough to step into the breach'.

The main difference in the Mackennal design lies in the portrait of the King. Could the original perhaps have met with Royal disapproval? The progressive proof illustrations of which more have been found since the last edition show similar vignettes of St. George and the Dragon, based on the model by Pistrucci used on the sovereign, but the style of lettering is modified and so is the spacing of Bradbury's signature. On the penultimate proof is written: "Proof as approved by W. Percy Thompson 19/10/16. George and the Dragon to be lighter top and bottom. Overprint to fit bar. Signature not to impinge". (Percy Thompson was a Commissioner of the Inland Revenue and later Deputy Chairman).

The new £1 notes were printed in photogravure by Waterlow Bros. and Layton despite an attempt by De La Rue to claim breach of contract by the Government. The £1 was issued on 22 February 1917 and the 10s. on 22 October 1918.

On the £1 The Times commented: "In design it is an entire departure from the old which as an artistic production it leaves far behind ... the most distinctive feature of the note is the splendid likeness of the King on the right hand, which on first glance appears to be embossed owing to the blending of its green and brown ... cases have come to light of the imitation of the old issue; it is doubtful whether even the most expert artist in forgery could reproduce the new. On the back is a coloured picture of the Houses of Parliament. This is intended as a further safeguard against the note being inadvertently thrown into the wastepaper basket or otherwise destroyed as a useless piece of paper ...".

It was around this time that serious concern was being felt over the shortage of silver coinage, mainly due to inflation and hoarding, and there were proposals to remedy this by the issue of 5s. notes. Bradbury himself was doubtful and the Bank of England totally opposed. "If 5s. notes are put into circulation, it will very soon become necessary to print notes for small denominations" they said (with prophetic accuracy!). Nonetheless the Government pressed ahead with the required bill and were only dissuaded at the very last minute from introducing it on 19 July 1918. Matters did not, however, rest there as the 5s. notes had already been prepared and by the end of the year designs for 2s.6d. and 1s. were in hand.

On 27 August 1919 Sir John Bradbury left the Treasury to become Principal British Delegate to the Reparation Commission and was succeeded by Sir Warren Fisher (formerly Chairman of the Board of Inland Revenue). Fisher viewed the currency notes "with a certain temperamental disinclination" but concluded in his memorandum to the Chancellor, Mr. Austen Chamberlain, that they should continue to bear the signature of the Secretary to the Treasury. "My signature", he added, "will need some compression!".

There were no more major changes to the Treasury notes, although a new style watermark was introduced into the £1 in 1923; then in 1927 following the Royal and Parliamentary Titles Act, the heading of both notes was changed to "UNITED KINGDOM OF GREAT BRITAIN AND *NORTHERN* IRELAND".

The other important event very early in the Warren Fisher period was the authorisation on 31 October 1919 "for the printing of 10 million notes of the approved design and bearing the signature of Sir N. F. Warren Fisher in each of the denominations 5s., 2s.6d. and 1s.". Ten days later the First World War ended and the notes were never needed.

Further information on Treasury notes will be found in an article by the author published in the *International Bank Note Society Journal* Vol. 20, No. 2 (1981).

JOHN BRADBURY (1914–1919)

John Bradbury was born in 1872 and entered the Civil Service in 1896, first in the Colonial Office and then the Treasury. After serving under Asquith and then Lloyd George (including help with the famous budget of 1909), Bradbury was appointed one of two permanent secretaries to the Treasury in 1913 along with Sir Thomas Heath.

At the outbreak of the First World War, Bradbury quickly realised the necessity of replacing gold with paper currency, and the banknotes which were issued by the Treasury carried his signature; they were immediately nicknamed 'Bradburys'. He remained the government's chief financial adviser during the war and left the Treasury on 27 August 1919 to become principal British delegate to the Reparation Commission. He was knighted in 1913, created the first Baron Bradbury in January 1925 and died in 1950.

FIRST ISSUE

1914 (7 August) ONE POUND

Emergency issue designed at the Royal Mint from sketches by Frederick Atterbury. Surface printed in sheets of 36 (4 × 9) on one side only by Waterlow Bros. and Layton from plates by Eyre and Spottiswoode, on stamp paper with watermark showing the simple version of the Royal Cypher and the word POSTAGE. First issue Treasury £1 notes measure 127 × 63.5mm (5 × 2½in.) and were legal tender until 12 June 1920.

The first 2½ million notes, which were delivered to the banks on Thursday 6 August for issue the following morning, can be identified by the large capital A, B or C prefix (see T1 and T2). Overall the issue totalled four million notes, according to H.M.S.O. records, so one can deduce that the total number of T3 to T7 notes was only 1½ million.

			EF	*VF*
T1	£1	Black on white		
		Prefix coding: Single capital letter and 6 digit number.		
		Quantity printed: 2½ million.		
		Serial letters:		
		A, B and C	1,200	550

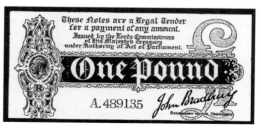

T1

T2

T2   **£1**   Black on white
Prefix coding: As T1 but with full stop omitted after letter.
Serial letters:
  A, B and C   from 1,500 (*VF*)

T3

T3   **£1**   Black on white
Prefix coding: Letter over number ('dot').

	from 1,500 (*VF*)	
Type 1: Four digits		
Type 2: Five digits	800	400
Type 3: Six digits	450	200
(*a variant has 6 digits in a smaller type similar to T5*).		
Type 4: Seven digits	800	400

Serial letters:
  A to Z (probably not inclusive)

BRADBURY (contd.)

			EF	VF

T4   **£1**   Black on white
Prefix coding: Letter over number ('dash').

	EF	VF
Type 1: Four digits	from 1,500 (*VF*)	
Type 2: Five digits	900	450
Type 3: Six digits	Not yet seen	
Type 4: Seven digits	Not yet seen	

Serial letters:
A to Z (probably not inclusive)

T5   **£1**   Black on white
Prefix coding: Letter over number ('dot' or 'dash') but
the digits are set in much smaller type.

	EF	VF
Type 1: Four digits	Not yet seen	
Type 2: Five digits	Not yet seen	
Type 3: Six digits ('dash')	1,000	500
Type 4: Seven digits ('dot')	1,200	650

Serial letters:
B and D (and possibly others)

T6   **£1**   Black on white
Prefix coding: Double letter over number ('dot') and
6 digits.
Serial letters:
BB, CC, DD, HH, JJ, LL (possibly others)   850   450

T7   **£1**   Black on white
            Prefix coding: Double letter over number ('dot' after
            No.) and 4 digits.
            Serial letters:
               LL (and possibly others)   from 1,500 (*VF*)

T7 notes are thought to have been used as replacements, although the general inconsistency of the system makes it possible that other methods were used to replace faulty notes. Some people have questioned whether notes with 5 digits were printed by De La Rue. There is no evidence to support this theory but bundles of printed notes might have been sent to them for numbering only.

Several minor varieties have been recorded over the years, which is hardly surprising given that the notes were produced at breakneck speed in such a short space of time using any numbering machines available. Under T5 type 3, for example, the author has seen a serial number where the N of No is 4mm high rather than the usual 3mm. Some notes may be found with the watermark sideways, inverted, or sideways inverted (or even non-existent) due to the practice of printing additional notes in the sheet margin. These varieties are likely to command a premium.

The following illustrations of type faces T2 and T7 have been reproduced from actual notes to facilitate indentification.

A.476039	ᴸ₃₆ № 0012
Type 1	Type 4/1
A 040564	ᴸ₇ № 21787
Type 2	Type 4/2
ᴳ₁₃ № 1791	ᴰ₈ № 002359
Type 3/1	Type 5/3
ᴮ₃₂ № 11955	ᴮ₁₃ № 0034287
Type 3/2	Type 5/4
ᴬ₂₉ № 015437	ᴸᴸ₃₄ № 000299
Type 3/3	Type 6
ᴮ₄₀ № 0071006	ᴸᴸ₃₄ NO. 0300
Type 3/4	Type 7

BRADBURY (contd.)

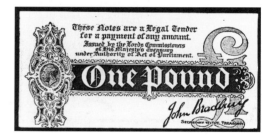

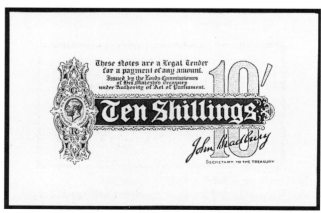

Bradbury proofs

1914 (14 August) TEN SHILLINGS

Emergency issue designed at the Royal Mint. Surface printed in sheets of 36 (4 × 9) on one side only by Waterlow Bros. and Layton (notes with 6 digit serial numbers) and by De La Rue and Co. (notes with 5 digit serial numbers) from plates by Eyre and Spottiswoode, on stamp paper with watermark of the Royal Cypher ('simple') and the word POSTAGE. First issue Treasury 10s. notes measure 127 × 63.5mm (5 × 2½in.) and were legal tender until 12 June 1920. The total quantity of notes printed is not known but was probably around 10 million.

			EF	VF
T8	**10s.**	Red on white (Waterlow)		
		Prefix coding: Letter over number ('dot') and 6 digits.		
		Serial letters:		
		S and T (and possibly others)	750	350

T9	**10s.**	Red on white (Waterlow)		
		Prefix coding: As T8 but the word 'No' is set in different typeface and precedes the prefix coding.		
		Serial letter:		
		A	300	150

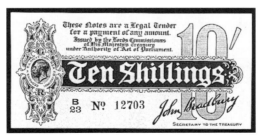

T10	**10s.**	Red on white (De La Rue)		
		Prefix coding: Letter over number ('dot') and 5 digits.		
		Serial letters:		
		A to Z (not inclusive)	750	350

BRADBURY (contd.)

As with the £1 note minor variations may be found and there may also be watermark varieties due to the fact that additional notes were probably printed in the sheet margin. Any varieties are likely to command a premium.

The following illustrations of typefaces T8 to T10 have been reproduced from actual notes to facilitate identification.

$$\tfrac{S}{25} \ N^{\underline{o}} \ \ 058890$$

Type 8

$$N^{\underline{o}} \ ^{\dagger}205949$$

Type 9

$$\tfrac{C}{10} \ N^{\underline{o}} \ \ 08991$$

Type 10

SECOND ISSUE

1914 (23 October) ONE POUND

Designed by George Eve. Surface-printed in sheets of 30 (5 × 6) on one side only by De La Rue and Co. on banknote paper manufactured by William Joynson and Co. with watermark of wavy lines incorporating the Royal Cypher, the ONE POUND denomination and the four British emblems: rose, thistle, shamrock and daffodil. Second issue Treasury £1 notes measure 149 × 85mm ($5\tfrac{7}{8}$ × $3\tfrac{1}{4}$in.) and were legal tender until 12 June 1920.

T11.1

T11.2

			EF	VF
T11	**£1**	Black on white		

Prefix coding:

Type 1: Letter over number and 5 digits — 250 100

Type 2: Letter and figure '1' over number and 5 digits — 250 100

Quantity printed: Not known.

Serial letters:

A to Z (probably not inclusive)

A1 to L1 (possibly not inclusive)

1915 (21 January) TEN SHILLINGS

Designed by George Eve. Surface-printed in sheets of 30 (5 × 6) on one side only by De La Rue and Co. on banknote paper manufactured by William Joynson and Co. with watermark of wavy lines incorporating the Royal Cypher, the 10/- denomination and the four British emblems: rose, thistle, shamrock and daffodil. Second issue Treasury 10s. notes measure 136 × 76mm ($5\frac{3}{8}$ × 3in.) and were legal tender until 12 June 1920.

T12 **10s.** Red on white (De La Rue)

Prefix coding:

Type 1: Letter over number and 5 digits — 200 80

Type 2: Letter and figure '1' over number and 5 digits — 200 80

Type 3: Letter and figure '2' over number and 5 digits — 200 80

Quantity printed: Not known.

Serial letters:

A to M (probably not inclusive)

A1 to Z1 (probably not inclusive)

A2, B2 and C2

BRADBURY (contd.)

T12.2

			EF	*VF*
T13	**10s.**	Red on white (Waterlow)		

Prefix coding:

	EF	*VF*
Type 1: Letter over number and 6 digits	225	100
Type 2: Letter and figure '1' over number and 6 digits	225	100

Quantity printed: Not known.

Serial letters:

N to Z (probably not inclusive)

Q1 to Z1 (probably not inclusive)

T13.1

THE DARDANELLES CAMPAIGN OVERPRINTS

Very little of real substance has been found to establish precisely how these rare and fascinating notes were calculated. The official Treasury minute in the Public Record Office states that the £1 and 10s. currency notes were issued for use by the entire British Military Expeditionary Forces in the Mediterranean and the Naval Expeditionary Forces from May to June 1915. Supplies of the notes were apparently sent to Malta and Alexandria, but whether these were the Gallipoli overprints, or when and for how long they were issued is still in dispute.

The student will find further information and conjecture in two articles by Fred Philipson in the *International Bank Note Society Journal* Vol. 10, No. 4 (1971) and Vol. 15, No. 4 (1976). Another useful article by Samuel Lachman appears in Vol. 15, No. 3 (1976).

According to the Inland Revenue records the notes were actually overprinted on 21 May 1915. The translation of the Arabic characters on the top line of the £1 reads 'Piastres silver 120' and on the bottom line 'Piastres silver one hundred and twenty'. The translation of the 10s. overprints reads 'Piastres silver 60' and 'Piastres silver sixty'.

				EF	VF
T14	**£1**	Black on white (red overprint) *Prefix coding:* Letter over number and 5 digits (as T11). *Quantity overprinted:* Not known. *Serial letters:* F , J , M, Y (and possibly others)		3,500	1,500
T15	**10s.**	Red on white (black overprint) *Prefix coding:* Letter over number and 6 digits (as T13). *Quantity overprinted:* Not known. *Serial letters:* Y and Z		750	250

BRADBURY (contd.)

T15

THIRD ISSUE

1917 (22 January) ONE POUND

Designed by Bertram Mackennal. Vignette of St. George and the Dragon based on the work of Benedetto Pistrucci for the Royal Mint. Printed by photogravure in sheets of 21 (3 × 7) by Waterlow Bros. and Layton on banknote paper manufactured by William Joynson and Co. with multiple watermark of Vandyck (diagonal) lines incorporating the Royal Cypher, the denomination ONE POUND and the four British emblems. Third issue Treasury £1 notes measure 151 × 84mm (5$\frac{15}{16}$ × 3$\frac{5}{16}$in.) and were legal tender until 1 August 1933.

			EF	VF
T16	**£1**	Brown, purple and green (shades) on white or cream paper		
		Prefix coding: Letter over number.		
		Quantity printed: 825 million.		
		Serial letters:		
		A	125	45
		B, C, D, E, F, G, H	85	30
		Z	100	35

Bradbury and Fisher £1 notes with serial 'Z' are from the bottom right-hand corner of the sheet giving a ratio of 20 to 1. It is thought that these 'Z' notes may have been used for control purposes.

1918 (22 October) TEN SHILLINGS

Designed by Bertram Mackennal. Printed by photogravure in sheets of 20 (4 × 5) by Waterlow Bros. and Layton on banknote paper manufactured by William Joynson and Co. with composite watermark incorporating the Royal Cypher, the denomination TEN SHILLINGS at the top and the four British emblems. Third issue 10s. notes measure 138 × 78mm ($5\frac{7}{16}$ × $3\frac{1}{16}$ in.) and were legal tender until 1 August 1933. The serial numbers of the first type are printed in black.

		EF	*VF*
T17	**10s.** Green, purple and brown on white paper *Prefix coding:* Letter over number ('dot'). *Quantity printed:* 100 million. *Serial letter (in* BLACK*):* A		300	150

T18	**10s.** Green, purple and brown on white paper *Prefix coding:* Letter over number ('dash'). *Quantity printed:* Included in T17 above. *Serial letter (in* BLACK*):* A		260	130

BRADBURY *(contd.)*

1919 (16 December) TEN SHILLINGS

As last issue but the serial number is now printed in red.

T19	**10s.**	Green, purple and brown on white paper *Prefix coding:* Letter over number ('dot'). *Quantity printed:* Included in T20 below. *Serial letters (in* RED*):* B and C		from 750 (*VF*)

T20	**10s.**	Green, purple and brown on white paper *Prefix coding:* Letter over number ('dash' or 'square dot'). *Quantity printed:* 200 million. *Serial letters (in* RED*):* B and C	200	100

1917 (1 December) FIVE SHILLINGS

Ratified (i.e. approved for distribution) on 21 February 1918. Designed by Bertram Mackennal. Printed by photogravure in sheets of 35 (5 × 7) by Waterlow Bros. and Layton on banknote paper manufactured by William Joynson and Co. with composite watermark incorporating the Royal Cypher and the denomination FIVE SHILLINGS. Treasury 5s. notes measure 127 × 76mm (5 × 3in.) and were distributed to the clearing banks in Great Britain and Ireland, but were not issued to the public. The notes were destroyed in November 1919 and the only examples traced are of proof status.

T21	**5s.**	Deep violet and green on white paper *Prefix coding:* Not known. *Quantity printed:* 7.9 million. *Serial letters:* A (probably)	—	—

1918 (November) HALF-CROWN

Designed by C. Howard with vignette of King George V by T. S. Harrison. Proofs were prepared by De La Rue and Co. and it seems that there was no production run of 2s.6d. notes signed by Bradbury. The only known example is a specimen note with the serial A/1 000000.

T22	**2s.6d.**	Olive-green and chocolate on white paper *Prefix coding:* Not known. *Quantity printed:* Not known. *Serial letters:* A 1	—	—

1918 (November) ONE SHILLING

Designed by C. Howard with vignette of King George V by T. S. Harrison. Proofs were prepared by De La Rue and Co. and it seems that there was no production run of 1s. notes signed by Bradbury. No example of the notes has been traced so far.

T23 **1s.** Green and brown on white paper
Prefix coding: Not known.
Quantity printed: Not known.
Serial letters:
Not known.

Bradbury 10 shillings Trial

BRADBURY (contd.)

Bradbury One Pound Trials

BRADBURY (contd.)

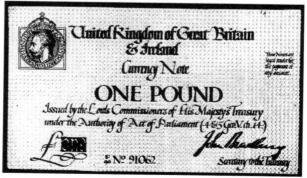

Bradbury One Pound Trials

NORMAN FENWICK WARREN FISHER (1919–1928)

Warren Fisher was born in 1879 and entered the Civil Service in 1903. His first post was at the Inland Revenue and in 1907 he became private secretary to the Chairman of the Board, Robert Chalmers. In 1912, he moved for a short time to the National Health Insurance Commission for England but returned the following year to Somerset House as a Commissioner of Inland Revenue. In 1918 he became Chairman. He was knighted in 1919 and on 1 October that year Sir Warren Fisher went as Permanent Secretary to the Treasury where he stayed until his retirement in 1939.

FIRST ISSUE

1919 (30 September) ONE POUND

Design, watermark and dimensions as for Bradbury T16 above. Printed by photogravure in sheets of 21 (3 × 7) by Waterlow Bros. and Layton on banknote paper manufactured by William Joynson and Co.

			EF	VF
T24	£1	Brown, purple and green (shades) on white or cream paper		
		Prefix coding: Letter over number.		
		Quantity printed: 1,150 million.		
		Serial letters:		
		K	50	20
		L , M , N , O , P , R , S , T , U , W , X , Y	45	20
		Z	50	20

For notes carrying the serial 'Z' see under T16.

FISHER (contd.)

1919 (30 September) TEN SHILLINGS

Design, watermark and dimensions as for Bradbury T19 above. Printed by photogravure in sheets of 20 (4 × 5) by Waterlow Bros. and Layton on banknote paper manufactured by William Joynson and Co. Serial numbers are in red.

			EF	VF
T25	**10s.**	Green, purple and brown on white paper		
		Prefix coding: Letter over number ('dot').		
		Quantity printed: 500 million.		
		Serial letters:		
		D	150	70
		E , F , G	150	70
		H	150	70
T26	**10s.**	Green, purple and brown on white paper		
		Prefix coding: Letter over number ('dash').		
		Quantity printed: Included in T17 above.		
		Serial letters:		
		D	100	50
		E , F , G	100	50
		H	100	50

1919 (28 November) FIVE SHILLINGS

Design, watermark and dimensions as for Bradbury T21 above. Printed by photogravure in sheets of 35 (5 × 7) by Waterlow Bros. and Layton on banknote paper manufactured by William Joynson and Co. Although Fisher 5s. notes were not officially issued a few evidently found their way into circulation, either by accident or possibly to test public opinion.

T27	**5s.**	Violet and green on white paper		
		Prefix coding: Letter over number.		
		Quantity printed: 10 million.		
		Serial letter:		
		B		from 2,500 (*VF*)

1919 (19 November) HALF-CROWN

Designs as for Bradbury T22 above. Surface-printed in sheets of 40 (4 × 10) by De La Rue and Co. on banknote paper manufactured by William Joynson and Co. with composite watermark incorporating the Royal Cypher and the denomination HALF-CROWN. Fisher 2s.6d. notes measure 117 × 75mm (4⅝ × 2¹⁵⁄₁₆in.) and were not officially issued, but a few evidently got out.

T28 **2s.6d.** Olive-green and chocolate on white paper
Prefix coding: Letter over number.
Quantity printed: 10 million.
Serial letter:
    A   from 3,000 (*VF*)

1919 (19 November) ONE SHILLING

Design as for Bradbury T23 above. Surface-printed in sheets of 49 (7 × 7) by De La Rue and Co. on banknote paper manufactured by William Joynson and Co. with composite watermark incorporating the Royal Cypher and the denomination ONE SHILLING. Fisher 1s. notes measure 104 × 66mm (4⅛ × 2⅞in.) and were not officially issued, but a few evidently got out.

T29 **1s.** Green and brown on white paper
Prefix coding: Letter over number.
Quantity printed: 10 million.
Serial letter:
    B   from 3,000 (*VF*)

FISHER (contd.)

SECOND ISSUE

1922 (6 November) TEN SHILLINGS

Design, watermark and dimensions as for Fisher T25 above. The difference is in the serial number which stands by itself with the word 'No' omitted. Printed by photogravure in sheets of 20 (4 × 5) by Waterlow and Sons (who replaced Waterlow Bros. and Layton in 1920) on banknote paper manufactured by Portals Ltd. (who replaced William Joynson).

			EF	VF
T30	**10s.**	Green, purple and brown on white paper		
		Prefix coding: Letter over number.		
		Quantity printed: 900 million.		
		Serial letters:		
		J	65	30
		K , L , M, N, O , P , R	65	30
		S	65	30

1923 (26 February) ONE POUND

Design and dimensions as for Fisher T24 above. The difference is in the watermark which is now composite so that the words ONE POUND appear at the top of each note. Printed by photogravure in sheets of 21 (3 × 7) by Waterlow and Sons on banknote paper manufactured by William Joynson and Co.

T31	**£1**	Brown, purple and green on white paper		
		Prefix coding: Letter and figure '1' over number ('dot').		
		Quantity printed: 1,700 million.		
		Serial letters:		
		A1	50	25
		B1, C1, D1, E1, F1, G1, H1, J1, K1, L1, M1, N1, O1, P1, R1	40	20
		Z1	50	25

EF   VF

T32   **£1**   Brown, purple and green on white paper
                 Prefix coding: Letter and figure '1' over number ('square
                 dot').
                 Quantity printed: Included in T31 above.
                 Serial letters:
                 Included in T31 above but most examples are H1 or M1   125   60
For notes carrying the serial 'Z' see under T16.

THIRD ISSUE

1927 (25 July) TEN SHILLINGS

Design, watermark and dimensions as for Fisher T30 above. The difference
is that following the Royal and Parliamentary Titles Act of 1927, the
wording on the notes was altered to read UNITED KINGDOM OF GREAT
BRITAIN AND NORTHERN IRELAND. Printed by photogravure in sheets of 20
(4 × 5) by Waterlow and Sons on banknote paper manufactured by Portals
Ltd.

T33   **10s.**   Green, purple and brown on white paper
                 Prefix coding: Letter over number.
                 Quantity printed: 250 million.
                 Serial letters:
                 S   85   40
                 T , U   85   40
                 W   85   40

T33a **10s.**   Faulty watermark.   from 250 (*VF*)
Some of the notes of this issue have a faulty watermark. The fault, when it
occurs, is on the fourth note of the third row, i.e. notes with serial prefix
numbers 12, 32, 52, 72 and 92. The fault is in the misshapen shamrock which
is not properly indented on its right-hand side.

FISHER (contd.)

1927 (25 July) ONE POUND

Design and dimensions as for Fisher T31 above. The difference is that following the Royal and Parliamentary Titles Act of 1927, the wording on the notes was altered to read UNITED KINGDOM OF GREAT BRITAIN AND NORTHERN IRELAND. Printed by photogravure in sheets of 20 (4 × 5) by Waterlow and Sons on banknote paper manufactured by Portals Ltd.

			EF	VF
T34	**£1**	Brown, purple and green on white paper		
		Prefix coding: Letter and figure '1' over number ('dot').		
		Quantity printed: 530 million.		
		Serial letters:		
		S1	60	30
		T1, U1, W1, X1	60	30
		Z1	70	35
T35	**£1**	Brown, purple and green on white paper		
		Prefix coding: Letter and figure '1' over number ('square dot').		
		Quantity printed: Included in T34 above.		
		Serial letters:		
		Included in T34 above but most examples are S1	125	60

For notes carrying the serial 'Z' see under T16.

The Bank of England took over the issue of 10s. and £1 notes from November 1928 but all Treasury notes from the Bradbury third issue onwards remained legal tender until the end of July 1933.

T34

Bank of England Notes

Bank of England Notes to 1928

The Bank of England was founded under a Royal Charter granted on 27 July 1694. During the reign of William and Mary (1689–1702) more money was needed to finance the War of the Grand Alliance against France. The idea for raising the money was put forward by a Scotsman, William Paterson, and a bill was drafted "for granting to their Majesties several rates and duties upon tunnage of ships and vessels and upon beer, ale and other liquors; for securing against certain recompenses and advantages in the said act mentioned, to such persons as shall voluntarily advance the sum of fifteen hundred thousand pounds towards carrying on the war against France". The recompenses and advantages were permission to set up "The Governor and Company of the Bank of England". The first governor was Sir John Houblon, his deputy was Mr. Michael Godfrey and there were 24 directors. Temporary offices were set up at the Mercers' Hall in Cheapside.

The first charter allowed the Bank to circulate notes up to the value of its capital of £1.2 million which was lent wholly to the government at 8% (yearly interest of £100,000). At this stage there was no guarantee of conversion of notes into gold, nor were the 'running cash notes', as they were called, given the status of legal tender.

The three cashiers were appointed on 30 July 1694. The head cashier was John Kendrick (at a salary of £200 a year) and his assistants were Robert Hedges and Thomas Madockes. Mr. Kendrick's term was the shortest on record. He found the duties of the office "too onerous" and was allowed to step down on 11 August. Thomas Speed was appointed in his place, holding the post until 1699, and he was succeeded by Thomas Madockes (1699–1739). By the end of 1694 the Bank's business had been transferred from the Mercers' Hall to the nearby Grocers' Hall where it remained until the move to Threadneedle Street in June 1734.

Within two years, however, the fledgling Bank was in trouble through no fault of its own. The problems arose from the passing of an Act in 1696 which ordered recoinage of the whole metallic currency. This had become hopelessly clipped and defaced, and, given the choice, people naturally wanted new sound money, although the poor were mostly unable to get it. Since the Bank's notes were not convertible they fell to a discount which at one stage was as high as 24%. Accounts submitted to Parliament on 4 December 1696 indicated that the £764,196 worth of notes outstanding were backed by only £35,664 in gold.

By March 1697 the position had greatly eased, the problems of the recoinage had been overcome and on 1 April the Bank's charter was renewed until 1711 by Act of Parliament which provided that "no other bank or any corporation in the nature of a bank shall be established by Act of Parliament in this Kingdom". A new subscription list was opened and the Bank's capital was increased by just over £1 million. The 1697 Act also contained a clause whereby the death penalty was to be imposed for forgery of the Bank's notes, though this was not to become a serious problem until the end of the 18th century.

In 1708 the Bank's monopoly was further strengthened by the veto of any notes payable on demand or at less than six months by joint stock banks with more than six partners. This was arguably the most important development in the early history of banking and was confirmed in the renewal of the Bank's charter in 1709 for 21 years and again when a 30 year renewal was enacted in 1713 following the Treaty of Utrecht.

The second major crisis for the Bank came in 1720 after the bursting of the 'South Sea Bubble'. Bankruptcy was rife, people naturally wished to get hold of their money and the queue of those wishing to withdraw gold from the Bank stretched down Ludgate Hill to Fleet Street. The situation was saved by the ingenious expedient of employing its own staff to withdraw money in large quantities and then take it round to the back of the Bank where it was redeposited! Thus the tills were kept open until the public alarm subsided. A similar ploy was used with equal effect in 1745 when Bonnie Prince Charlie was marching on London.

The Bank's charter was renewed again in 1742, 1764 and 1781. The main development during these years was the rapid growth of small notes from the country banks (of fewer than six partners), since Bank of England notes did not circulate much outside London. An attempt to stem the tide of paper was made in 1765 when it became illegal to issue notes for less than £1 other than on demand in Scotland, and the same was applied in England from 1775. Two years later this provision was extended when all notes of £1 and above and less than £5 had to carry the names and places of abode of persons to whose order they were made, and the signature attested by at least one witness. The effect was to reduce the supply of £1 notes from the country banks very considerably (although this particular restriction did not apply to Scotland).

During this period the Bank enjoyed almost uninterrupted prosperity, but in February 1793 war was again declared between France and England and there followed a collapse of confidence. More than threequarters of the 400 country banks were forced to close in the next two or three years despite the attempts by the Bank to alleviate the crisis. Napoleon was still relatively unknown but French activities were regularly reported and rumoured and finally on Monday 27 February 1797 the Bank itself stopped payment in cash.

The Bank Restriction Act became law on 3 May 1797 under which the Bank was forbidden to pay cash for sums of 20 shillings or more to any creditor or use cash for any payment except to the Army or Navy, or Ordnance on a Privy Council order. It was, however, stated that payment in the Bank's notes might be "legal tender by consent"—that is if they were freely offered and accepted as such. The act was intended to be a temporary measure. In the event the Bank did not resume full cash payments until

1 May 1821, although they did sell captured Spanish Dollars (pieces of eight), held in their vaults as bullion. The coins were stamped with a small oval containing the head of George III and could be bought by the public at 4s.9d. each.

. The famous £1 and £2 notes date from the Restriction. First they carried the name of Abraham Newland (they were nicknamed Newlands) and from 1807 that of Henry Hase. But confidence gradually returned and this was reflected in the fact that by 1810 the number of county banks had risen to more than 700. From November 1816 the Bank began to ease its restrictions which it was entitled to do on due notice, and notes for less than £5 issued before 1812 were exchangeable for cash. By September 1817 soon after the gold sovereign had become legal tender, the Bank was paying out on all notes issued prior to January 1817. Unfortunately the position again deteriorated and restrictions had to be imposed until the end of January 1820. It was during this period that a great deal of time and effort was expended in trying to produce notes which were proof against forgery. The best known of the experiments are those by Augustus Applegarth and Edward Cowper. Further details can be found on page 149 and the whole story is admirably told in *As Good As Gold—300 Years of British Bank Note Design* by Virginia Hewitt and John Keyworth.

Meanwhile legislation had been passed which put a fixed time on permission to issue notes below £5 to bearer on demand. This was to be two years after the resumption of cash payments (1 May 1823). However, by an Act of 1822 this permission was extended to 1833 for all banks. It was not a wise decision and a massive expansion of credit followed. By 1825 dozens of country banks were collapsing, the most serious failure being that of Pole Thornton and Co. in September of that year. The consequences were so severe that the Bank of England had to use all its resources to stem the panic—even to the extent of using an old stock of 600,000 £1 notes from the Restriction period. In December 1825 the Bank's reserves fell to as little as £14 million compared to £13½ million in 1824.

It was these events that led to a series of Acts over the next 18 years on which the modern banking system is based. The first of these in 1826 underlined the belief in the need for reliable joint stock banks. The Bank of England's monopoly was limited to a radius of 65 miles of London, thus making it possible for joint stock banks with more than six partners to operate outside the limit. These banks were able to issue their own notes for £5 and above. Existing notes of less than £5 payable to bearer on demand were to be redeemed not later than 5 April 1829. At the same time the Bank of England was allowed to open branches anywhere in the country and the first such branch opened in Gloucester on 19 July 1826.

In the 1833 Bank Charter Act, Bank of England notes were made legal tender for the first time on all sums above £5 except at the Bank itself so long as they were convertible into legal coin. This apparently strange proviso was to enable individual £5 notes to be changed into gold for the payment of wages. The Act also permitted the establishment of joint stock banks within 65 miles of the capital provided that they were for deposit only and did not issue their own notes. The first bank to take advantage of this was the London and Westminster which opened in London in March 1834.

The 1830s were times of boom and speculation, especially in railways, and credit was extended on a massive scale leading to inevitable collapses. The country note issue expanded by 50% in 1836 alone and it was against this background that Sir Robert Peel introduced the most far reaching Act of all, the Bank Charter Act 1844 (passed on 19 July). This finally put a stop to the free-for-all in banking and put strict controls on note issuing. By this stage there were more than 200 private banks and 72 joint stock banks in business. Under the Act new banks were forbidden to issue notes, limits were set on existing banks and if a bank were taken over or wound up, the right of issue was forfeited. Two thirds of the lapsed note issuing limit passed to the Bank of England and just over 75 years later the final country note issue ceased when Fox Fowler and Co. of Wellington, Somerset, merged with Lloyds Bank in October 1921.

Despite the railway crisis of 1847, the American crisis of 1857, the Overend Gurney Bank crash of 1866 and the Baring crisis of 1890, the standing of the Bank of England was never seriously challenged following the 1844 Bank Charter Act. As Richard B. Kimball wrote in *Popular Monthly* in 1882: "The credit of England and the credit of the Bank of England are convertible terms".

Early Issues

RUNNING CASH NOTES

Running cash notes derive from the goldsmith notes which had been widely used by merchants from the reign of Charles I. The running cash note was a receipt for a deposit made out to bearer so that he could use it in a business transaction or present it to the Bank for gold or silver. The first two Chief Cashiers were:

JOHN KENDRICK (1694) AND THOMAS SPEED (1694–99)
(The 1st and 2nd Chief Cashiers)

The notes were at first written entirely by hand on ordinary paper purchased from stationers—a practice which soon ceased because of forgery. These notes could be part-paid. The holder could draw £5 from a note issued for £10 and have it duly recorded on the note, retaining the note as a receipt for the remaining £5 still on deposit with the Bank. At first running cash notes were issued for odd amounts but before long they were made out for regular amounts. No examples are known to be in private hands.

ACCOMPTABLE NOTES

Introduced four days after the running cash notes, these were certificates of deposit and were not intended to serve as banknotes. They gave the depositor the right to "draw notes" on the Bank. Such withdrawals were then endorsed on the accomptable note. At a later date special forms were prepared by the Bank with a check pattern. The drawn notes were written by depositors on these forms which thus became an early version of the modern cheque.

SEALED BILLS

These were not banknotes in the strict sense as they were promissory notes, normally bearing interest issued against deposits or pledged assets. If they were intended to circulate, then they were not a success and within 20 years went out of use altogether.

It is interesting to record that running cash notes, accomptable notes and sealed bills were all introduced in the first week of the Bank of England's existence. The first meeting of the Court of Directors of the bank on 27 July 1694 was concerned with the "method of giving receipts for running cash..." and the first decision was that running cash notes should be issued.

PRINTED AND PART-PRINTED NOTES

In 1695 there was a short-lived issue of printed denominations of £5, £10, £20, £50 and £100. According to Mackenzie in *The Bank of England Note*, the order was placed on 5 June 1695 with the Bank's stationer, William Staresmore. No sooner had they been issued than a forgery appeared and they had to be withdrawn. The Bank then had the idea of using water-marked paper and in 1697 paper with a watermark of looped border and scroll on the left and the words Bank of England at the bottom was produced by a Berkshire papermaker, Rice Watkins. The first partially printed notes of the Bank were issued soon afterwards. They have a medallion of Britannia seated and holding a spear and olive branch, possibly the work of John Surt. For the most part these notes only circulated within a 20 mile radius of London. The earliest surviving examples are signed by:

THOMAS MADOCKES (1699–1739)
(The 3rd Chief Cashier)

Notes continued to be issued for handwritten amounts, but in 1707 the design of the Britannia medallion was modified to show a foliate border surround and from 1725, 14 denominations were printed by copper plate. In 1725 the Bank began using special paper produced by Henry Portal. Denominations were produced for £20, £30, £40, £50, £60, £70, £80, £90, £100, £200, £300, £400, £500 and £1,000. Dates of first issue vary.

JAMES COLLIER AND DANIEL RACE (1739–1751)
(The 4th and 5th Chief Cashiers)

Notes continued to be issued in the 14 denominations above. By 1745 notes were all printed in round figures. However, the word pounds was not printed so that an odd amount could still be written by hand if required. The Bank has one such note for £28.10s. on which the words "eight pounds ten shillings" have been written after the printed "Twenty".

DANIEL RACE AND ELIAS SIMES (1751–1759)
(The 5th and 6th Chief Cashiers)

From 1752 the handwritten name of the payee was usually that of the Chief Cashier. In 1759 two further denominations for £10 and £15 were issued and for the first time the word "pound" or "pounds" was printed after the amount. Other denominations continued to have "pounds" handwritten until the end of the century.

DANIEL RACE (1759–1775)
(The 5th Chief Cashier)

Notes continued to be issued for the 16 denominations above and in 1765 a note for £25 was added with the words "pounds" printed on it.

CHARLES JEWSON (1775–1777)
(The 7th Chief Cashier)

There were no developments of significance during Charles Jewson's short period in office.

Note: Since very few banknotes prior to the Newland period are known to have survived in private hands, a formal catalogue reference is not thought to be relevant. Thereafter each Chief Cashier from Newland to Harvey is allocated a master number covering all his notes. In most cases collectors will count themselves lucky to obtain even a single example of each Chief Cashier.

B200a

ABRAHAM NEWLAND (1778–1807)
(The 8th Chief Cashier)

Abraham Newland, the son of a miller and baker of Southwark, entered service in 1748. He succeeded Charles Jewson as Chief Cashier on 8 January 1778 and held office until September 1807. His name became a household word during the restriction period from 1797 and £1 notes were often referred to as Newlands. History relates that his commitment to business was such that he never slept away from the Bank. A confirmed bachelor, he amassed a fortune of £200,000, declined a pension and was instead given a piece of silver plate to the value of 1,000 guineas.

There are several varieties of Newland notes. From 1752 until 1781 the handwritten name of the payee was usually, but not invariably, that of the Chief Cashier. In fact, the oldest Newland note so far recorded in private hands, a £50 dated 13 April 1780, is not payable to Newland. From 1782 the Chief Cashier's name was used exclusively until 1855 when notes were made payable simply to bearer. In 1793 the economic difficulties caused by the Napoleonic War with France made small denominations necessary, starting with a £5 note. This was followed in 1797 by the £1 and £2 notes, which were issued on 2 March.

1778

Printed by copper plate in black and white on paper produced by Henry Portal. Denominations of £10, £15, £20, £25, £30, £40, £50, £60, £70, £80, £90, £100, £200, £300, £400, £500 and £1,000 were produced. The £60, £70, £80, £90 and £400 notes were no longer issued after 1803.

1793–1807

			Fine
B200a	£1	Black on white 1797 (handwritten number, date, cashier and signatures)	—
B200b	£1	Black on white 1798–1801 (smaller plate, printed cashier's name)	—
B200c	£1	Black on white 1801–1803 (standard size, new watermark)	from 850
B200d	£1	Black on white 1803–1807 (as type 'c' with value in watermark)	from 850
B200e	£2	Black on white 1797 (as type 'a' £1)	—
B200f	£2	Black on white 1798–1801 (as type 'b' £1)	—
B200g	£2	Black on white 1801–1803 (as type 'c' £1)	from 2,500
B200h	£2	Black on white 1803–1805 (as type 'd' £1)	—
B200j	£2	Black on white 1805–1807 (Bank of England head)	—
B200k	£5	Black on white (from 18 April 1793)	—
B200l	£10	Black on white 1798–1801 (as type 'b' £1)	—
B200m	£10	Black on white 1805–1807 (Bank of England head)	—
B200n	£15	Black on white	—

Examples of the £10 (B200l) and £15 notes were sold at auction by Sotheby's on 6 October 1989, but very few of the denominations above £2 are in private hands and other varieties may exist.

B200b

B200g

NEWLAND (contd.)

B200k

B200l

B200m

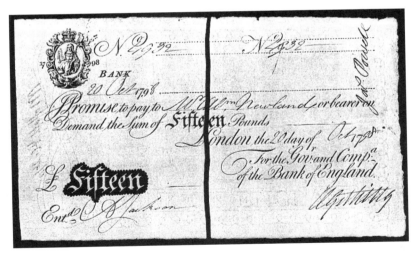

B200n

HENRY HASE (1807–1829)
(The 9th Chief Cashier)

Henry Hase was known as the reluctant Chief Cashier. He came into office only because of the disgrace of the second cashier, Robert Aslett, who was found guilty of embezzling half a million pounds in 1803. Aslett had taken Exchequer Bills amounting to £200,000 and had lodged these as security for advances with a lottery office keeper in Cornhill. He escaped the death penalty and was imprisoned in Newgate until 1820 when he was pardoned on condition he left the country. Hase was not dedicated to the Bank in the way that Abraham Newland had been and died in 1829 at a comparatively young age.

1807

Printed by copper plate on paper produced by Henry Portal. From 1807 the name of the Chief Cashier was printed as payee. From 1808 the dates and serial numbers were printed, so the only part of the note not printed was the signature(s). This remained the case until 1853.

			Fine
B201a	£1	Black on white (handwritten date, countersigned)	—
B201b	£1	Black on white (handwritten date, not countersigned)	—
B201c	£1	Black on white (printed date & serial numbers)	from 450
B201d	£1	Black on white (1825–26 emergency issue)	from 450

The emergency issue can be identified by the date at the top reading 1821, although the actual date of issue is four or five years later.

B201c

B201g

B201e	£2	Black on white (handwritten date, countersigned)	—
B201f	£2	Black on white (handwritten date, not countersigned)	—
B201g	£2	Black on white (printed date & serial numbers)	from 1,250
B201h	£5	Black on white (handwritten)	—
B201j	£5	Black on white (printed date & serial numbers)	—

B201j

HASE (contd.)

Hase notes were also issued in the following 12 denominations:

£10, £15, £20, £25, £30, £40, £50, £100, £200, £300, £500 and £1,000. The £15 and £25 notes were withdrawn from 1822. Very few examples are known to be in private hands.

Following the Bank Act of 1826 when the joint stock banks were permitted to operate outside a 65 mile radius of London, the Bank of England was able to open branches and branch notes date from this period. Very few have survived from the 19th century and they are impossible to price.

Henry Hase branch notes were issued from the following nine offices:

GLOUCESTER (opened 19 July 1826)
MANCHESTER (opened 21 September 1826)
SWANSEA (opened 23 October 1826)
BIRMINGHAM (opened 1 January 1827)
LIVERPOOL (opened 2 July 1827)
BRISTOL (opened 12 July 1827)
LEEDS (opened 23 August 1827)
EXETER (opened 17 December 1827)
NEWCASTLE (opened 21 April 1828)

Early 19th Century Bank of England Trials

THOMAS RIPPON (1829–1835)
(The 10th Chief Cashier)

Thomas Rippon was born in Up Ottery, Devon, in 1759, the son of a baptist minister. He entered service with the Bank in 1782. Following the dismissal of Robert Aslett in 1803, Rippon was promoted from third clerk in the drawing office to second cashier. When Henry Hase became Chief Cashier, Rippon was appointed as his chief assistant in 1807. Rippon became Chief Cashier at the age of 70 in 1829 and remained in office until his death on 10 August 1835. He declared himself nowhere so happy as in his business and supposedly took only one holiday during his entire career with the Bank, 1835.

1829

Plate printed on paper manufactured by Henry Portal.

B202a **£5**	Black on white		from 1,500 (*VF*)
B202b **£10**	Black on white		—

Rippon notes were also issued in the following nine denominations:

£20, £30, £40, £50, £100, £200, £300, £500 and £1,000. The £40 note was withdrawn in 1851 and the £30 in 1852. Very few examples are known to be in private hands.

B202a

B202b

Rippon branch notes were issued from the following 13 offices:

BIRMINGHAM
BRISTOL
EXETER (CLOSED 30 APRIL 1834)
GLOUCESTER
HULL (opened 2 January 1829)
LEEDS
LIVERPOOL

MANCHESTER
NEWCASTLE
NORWICH (opened 19 November 1829)
PLYMOUTH (opened 1 May 1834)
PORTSMOUTH (opened 16 May 1834)
SWANSEA

MATTHEW MARSHALL (1835–1864)
(The 11th Chief Cashier)

No biographical information is available on the career of Matthew Marshall. He was in office during the major commercial crisis of 1857 when two banks in Liverpool failed, and by November of that year the Bank of England was virtually the only bank prepared to discount bills of exchange.

There are three different types of Marshall notes. The first series from 1835–53 is the same as Thomas Rippon with various handwritten signatures. From 1853–55 notes were printed bearing signatures of bank officials: J. Vautin, H. Bock, J. Ferraby, J. Williams and J. Luson. From 1855 the third series replaced the name of the Chief Cashier with the words "I promise to pay the Bearer on Demand". At the same time Marshall's signature was introduced into the watermark and the vignette of Britannia was redesigned by Daniel Maclise R.A. In 1860 new signatures of bank officials were introduced: W. P. Gattie, T. Kent and C. T. Whitmel (all printed as before).

B203a – Gattie signature

1835

Plate printed on paper manufactured by Henry Portal.

B203a	£5	Black on white (handwritten signature)	from 1,500 (*VF*)
B203b	£5	Black on white (printed signature)	from 1,500 (*VF*)
B203c	£5	Black on white (watermark signature)	from 1,500 (*VF*)
B203d	£10	Black on white	—

B203d

Marshall notes were also issued in the following denominations:

£20, £30, £40, £50, £100, £200, £300, £500 and £1,000. The £40 note was withdrawn in 1851 and the £30 in 1852. Very few examples are known to be in private hands.

Marshall branch notes were issued from the following 13 offices:

BIRMINGHAM	LIVERPOOL
BRISTOL	MANCHESTER
GLOUCESTER (closed 28 February 1849)	NEWCASTLE
HULL	NORWICH (closed 31 March 1852)
LEEDS	PORTSMOUTH
LEICESTER (opened 1 January 1844)	SWANSEA (closed 28 February 1859)

A Marshall £5 note issued in Manchester on 16 January 1854 was sold at auction in 1989.

WILLIAM MILLER (1864–1866)
(The 12th Chief Cashier)

No biographical information is available on the career of William Miller. There appears to be no such thing as a "Miller" note. When Marshall's signature was removed from the watermark, for unknown reasons Miller's signature was not substituted. The date therefore determines the Chief Cashier together with the printed signatures of bank officials W. P. Gattie, T. Kent or C. T. Whitmel.

1864

Plate printed on paper manufactured by Henry Portal.

B204a **£5**   Black on white   from 3,000 (*VF*)
B204b **£10**   Black on white   —

"Miller" notes were also issued in the following seven denominations:

£20, £50, £100, £200, £300, £500 and £1,000. Very few examples are known to be in private hands.

"Miller" branch notes were probably issued from the following 10 offices:

BIRMINGHAM	LIVERPOOL
BRISTOL	MANCHESTER
HULL	NEWCASTLE
LEEDS	PLYMOUTH
LEICESTER	PORTSMOUTH

B205a

GEORGE FORBES (1866–1873)
(The 13th Chief Cashier)

No biographical information is available on the career of George Forbes. There are two types of Forbes notes. The first contains his signature in the watermark while the printed signatures are those of other bank staff: H. Dixon, T. Puzey or W. O. Wheeler. From 1 November 1870 the printed signature of the Chief Cashier appears on all Bank of England notes together with his title underneath.

1866

Plate printed on paper manufactured by Henry Portal. Notes printed two to a sheet and cut to give one straight edge and three deckle edges.

B205a **£5**	Black on white (watermark signature)	from 1,500 (*VF*)
B205b **£5**	Black on white (signed G. Forbes)	from 1,750 (*VF*)
B205c **£10**	Black on white (watermark signature)	—
B205d **£10**	Black on white (signed G. Forbes)	—

B205c

FORBES (contd.)

Forbes notes were also issued in the following seven denominations:

£20, £50, £100, £200, £300, £500 and £1,000. Very few examples are known to be in private hands.

Forbes branch notes were issued from the following 10 offices:

BIRMINGHAM	LIVERPOOL
BRISTOL	MANCHESTER
HULL	NEWCASTLE
LEEDS	PLYMOUTH
LEICESTER (closed 29 February 1872)	PORTSMOUTH

B206a – London

FRANK MAY (1873–1893)
(The 14th Chief Cashier)

Frank May was born in Hull on 21 August 1832 and entered service with the Bank in 1852, following in the steps of his father, Henry May. He rose to become Chief Cashier on 30 July 1873. However, in 1893, he was dismissed, having "totally misconceived the nature of his trust" by favouring certain customers, mostly in the Stock Exchange, without the permission of the Governor. May had apparently allowed unauthorised overdrafts and had waived interest payments on other accounts. He ended his days in obscurity and died at Batcombe in Somerset in February 1897. He left £2,620-15s.-1d. The Reeves committee of enquiry which investigated the affair concluded that the Chief Cashier should become the highest paid official of the Bank thereafter.

1873

Plate printed on paper manufactured by Henry Portal. Notes printed two to a sheet and cut to give one straight edge and three deckle edges.

B206a	£5	Black on white	from 800 (*VF*)
B206b	£10	Black on white	—

May notes were also issued in the following seven denominations:

£20, £50, £100, £200, £300, £500 and £1,000. Very few examples are known to be in private hands.

May branch notes were issued from the following nine offices:

BIRMINGHAM*   MANCHESTER*
BRISTOL*   NEWCASTLE*
HULL   PLYMOUTH
LEEDS   PORTSMOUTH
LIVERPOOL*

*Notes from branches marked with an asterisk are known to exist in private collections.

MAY (contd.)

B206a – Birmingham branch

B206a – Newcastle on Tyne branch

HORACE GEORGE BOWEN (1893–1902)
(The 15th Chief Cashier)

Horace Bowen served as Chief Accountant from 1888 and succeeded Frank May on 9 November 1893. The immediate consequence of May's disgrace was the setting up of a committee to report on "Officers emoluments and safeguards for due control of advances and overdrafts and accounts generally, and the manner in which the services of the committee in daily waiting may be best employed".

1893

Plate printed on paper manufactured by Henry Portal. Notes printed two to a sheet and cut to give one straight edge and three deckle edges.

			EF	VF
B207a **£5**	Black on white		2,000	800
B207b **£10**	Black on white		—	—

Bowen notes were also issued in the following six denominations:

£20, £50, £100, £200, £500 and £1,000. Very few examples are known to be in private hands.

B207a – London

Bowen branch notes were issued from the following nine offices:

BIRMINGHAM MANCHESTER
BRISTOL NEWCASTLE
HULL PLYMOUTH
LEEDS PORTSMOUTH
LIVERPOOL

BOWEN (contd.)

B207a – Liverpool branch

An example of a higher value Bowen note

JOHN GORDON NAIRNE (1902–1918)
(The 16th Chief Cashier)

Gordon Nairne entered Bank service in 1880 and was appointed Chief Cashier in 1902. He became Comptroller in 1918 and was a Director from 1925–1931.

1902

Plate printed on paper manufactured by Henry Portal. Notes printed two to a sheet and cut to give one straight edge and three deckle edges.

			EF	VF
B208a	£1	Black on white (unissued)	from 2,500 (EF)	
B208b	£5	Black on white	200	75
B208c	£10	Black on white	400	200
B208d	£20	Black on white*	1,500	750
B208e	£50	Black on white*	1,500	750
B208f	£100	Black on white*	2,000	1,000
B208g	£200	Black on white	—	—
B208h	£500	Black on white	—	—
B208i	£1,000	Black on white	—	—

For prefix details and dates of Nairne £5 notes see Appendix B. Prices quoted are for Nairne notes from 1913 onwards. Notes from the earlier period are likely to carry a substantial premium.

During the summer of 1914 it became increasingly clear to both the Treasury and the Bank of England that some form of paper money of lower denomination than £5 would have to be substituted for the gold sovereign. The question was who would issue it. The Bank had no doubts about its claim and made preparations. The Bank £1 note (B208a) in its unissued proof form is a sought after rarity in the English series and fewer than a dozen copies are known to exist. There is also reported to be an example with the signature of E. M. Harvey.

NAIRNE (contd.)

Nairne branch notes were issued (£5 in ascending order of rarity) from the following nine offices:

1. LEEDS
2. MANCHESTER
3. LIVERPOOL
4. BIRMINGHAM
5. NEWCASTLE
6. HULL
7. PLYMOUTH
8. BRISTOL
9. PORTSMOUTH
   (closed 30 April 1914)

*Higher denomination notes from the branches are normally extremely rare, but in the case of Nairne an extraordinary 'hoard' of 136 notes was discovered by a Derbyshire gentleman in 1989. These included £5, £10, £20, £50 and £100 notes, mostly from Manchester to a face value of just over £9,000. The notes realised £92,000 and full details can be found in the catalogue of sale on 14 September 1989 from Messrs. A. F. Brock & Co., in Manchester. For Nairne only, notes marked with an asterisk are priced for Manchester rather than for London examples.

For classification of specimen notes and errors see pages 140–145.

B208b – Portsmouth

B208e – Manchester

B208f – Manchester

B208f – Portsmouth

ERNEST MUSGRAVE HARVEY (1918–1925)
(The 17th Chief Cashier)

Ernest Harvey entered Bank service in 1885. He became Deputy Chief Cashier in 1902 and Chief Cashier in 1918. He was appointed Comptroller in 1925. He was a Director from 1928–1929 and Deputy Governor from 1929–1936. He was knighted in 1920 and created a Baronet in 1933. Among his other honours were the C.B.E., Chevalier of the Legion of Honour 1918 and Chevalier of the Order of Leopold of Belgium 1919.

1918

Plate printed on paper manufactured by Henry Portal. Notes printed two to a sheet and cut to give one straight edge and three deckle edges.

			EF	*VF*
B209a	£5	Black on white (from 10 May 1918)	100	50
B209b	£10	Black on white	190	100
B209c	£20	Black on white	750	300
B209d	£50	Black on white	750	300
B209e	£100	Black on white	1,100	500
B209f	£200	Black on white	—	—
B209g	£500	Black on white	from 5,000 (*VF*)	
B209h	£1,000	Black on white		

For prefix details and dates of Harvey £5 notes see Appendix B.

Harvey branch notes were issued (£5 in ascending order of rarity) from the following eight offices:

1. LEEDS
2. LIVERPOOL
3. MANCHESTER
4. HULL
5. NEWCASTLE
6. BIRMINGHAM
7. PLYMOUTH
8. BRISTOL

For classification of specimen notes and errors see pages 140–145.

HARVEY (contd.)

B209a – Leeds

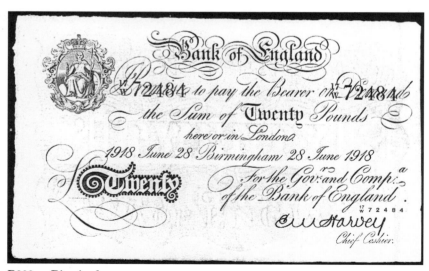

B209c – Birmingham

B209d

B209e – Birmingham

HARVEY (contd.)

B209f

B209g

B209g

B209h

Bank of England Notes from 1928

The Bank of England assumed responsibility for the printing and issue of currency notes on 22 November 1928 under the *Currency and Banknotes Act 1928* and in July 1933 the Treasury notes were withdrawn from circulation.

The Bank's first issue (Series A) of green £1 notes and red-brown 10s. notes, referred to by collectors as Britannia notes, was signed by the Chief Cashier C. P. Mahon (pronounced Ma-hon), and joined the existing high-denomination notes of £5 and above.

In June 1931, after consulting the Royal Mint Advisory Committee, the Bank invited three artists to compete with a view to future note designs, Stephen Gooden, Frederick Landseer Griggs and Kruger Gray. As a result Gooden was appointed as the Bank's designer, but the various essays that he produced during the 1930s were not taken up.

In 1940, following the outbreak of war, the colour of the £1 and 10s. notes was changed to blue and mauve respectively and a metal thread, the invention of Mr. S. B. Chamberlain, General Manager of the Bank's Printing Works, was inserted.

In 1943, following the appearance of German forgeries, it was decided to withdraw the denominations above £5. It was 20 years before the £10 was to reappear, nearly 30 years before the country again had a £20 note and nearly 40 years to the return of the £50 note.

One problem that the Bank faced during the war was the difficulty in transporting coinage. In view of this small denomination notes of 2s.6d. and 5s. were prepared, but they were not needed. The notes were supposedly all destroyed after the war, but a few specimens survived and have found their way into the hands of collectors.

In 1948 £1 and 10s. notes of the pre-war colours, green and red-brown, were again issued and for a short time were unthreaded to use up the old stocks of paper. Subsequently all Bank of England notes incorporated the now familiar metal thread as a security precaution.

During the 1950s Stephen Gooden prepared a new series of notes depicting the first Governor of the Bank, Sir John Houblon. They were not issued. He followed this with a series featuring a Lion and Key and the helmeted head of Britannia (Series B) from which the £5 was issued in 1957 to replace the traditional white fiver.

Meanwhile in July 1956 it was announced that H.M. The Queen had agreed to her portrait being included on the new series of notes. Stephen Gooden had died on 21 September 1955 and the designs for this issue

(Series C), known to collectors as the Portrait series, were undertaken by Robert Austin.

On 19 November 1959 the Bank formally announced that the new notes would appear early in 1960 and on 17 March that year the £1 appeared, followed some 18 months later by the 10s. Then in 1963 came the £5 and in 1964 the £10. These last two were the work of Reynolds Stone who was retained by the Bank from 1959, and on the £5 note he used his daughter as the model for the child Britannia on the reverse.

Soon afterwards work began on a new more ambitious set of designs by Harry Eccleston who had joined the Bank in 1958. These became the Series D notes, known to collectors as the Pictorial series. The reverse of each note carries an historical scene although the first of them, the 10s. featuring Sir Walter Raleigh, was unissued. The £20 (first issued in 1970) shows a statue of William Shakespeare with the balcony scene from *Romeo and Juliet*; the £5 (1971) features the Duke of Wellington and a battle scene from the Peninsular War; the £10 (1975) depicts Florence Nightingale and a hospital scene from the Crimean War; and the last in the series, the £1 (1978), had Sir Isaac Newton with his telescope sitting under an apple tree. The £1 note was replaced by the £1 coin in 1983 and finally ceased to be legal tender in 1988. During this period some changes were also made to the colouring and security threads of the other notes.

In October 1988, the Bank announced that work had started on a fresh series of notes (Series E), designed by Roger Withington who had succeeded Harry Eccleston as Artist Designer in January 1983. The notes are scheduled for issue over a four year period 1990–1994 and are smaller than the Series D notes. The first of them, the £5, was issued on 7 June 1990 and featured George Stephenson (and various locomotives with which he was associated). It also included a new portrait of H.M. The Queen. The bank has also given some information on subsequent notes: The £20 (scheduled for 1991) will feature Michael Faraday, the physicist and chemist in the bicentenary of his birth. The £10 (scheduled for 1992) will feature the novelist, Charles Dickens. The £50 (scheduled for 1994) will feature the first Governor, Sir John Houblon, in the Bank's tercentenary year.

SERIES A (BRITANNIA) 1928–62

On 22 November 1928 the Bank of England £1 note was reintroduced after a gap of more than 100 years and the 10s. note was introduced for the first time. The new banknotes were signed by the Chief Cashier, C. P. Mahon, and replaced the various Treasury notes issued since 1914.

The designs, approved in 1927, were a collective effort by the architect, W. M. Keesey (responsible for the reverse of both notes) and other experts inside and outside the Bank. The obverse of both notes showed the medallion of Britannia by Daniel Maclise originally used for the high-denominations from 1855. Keesey's reverse of the £1 showed the south front of the Bank prior to rebuilding together with vignettes of St. George and the dragon used by Benedetto Pistrucci in his design for the sovereign. These were contained in swirls of acanthus leaves of pale green, blue and mauve.

A similar background in red-brown was used for the reverse of the 10s. surrounding the two value tablets.

The notes were plate-printed in sheets of 21 (7 × 3) at St. Luke's Works, Old Street, London, on banknote paper manufactured by Portals Ltd., with a watermark of wavy lines and the helmeted head of Britannia facing right. Series A—or Britannia £1 notes as they are called by collectors—measure 150.7mm × 84.4mm (5$\frac{15}{16}$ × 3$\frac{15}{16}$in.) and were legal tender until 28 May 1962. The 10s. notes measure 138mm × 78mm (5$\frac{7}{16}$ x 3$\frac{1}{16}$in.) and were also printed in sheets of 21 (7 × 3). They were legal tender until 29 October 1962. In a letter to the author in 1989 the Bank has revealed for the first time that a total of 10,500 million Series A 10s. and 20,000 million £1 notes were issued. Quantities printed for each prefix are the author's own estimates and must be regarded as approximate within the overall total.

The listings that follow are arranged under the names of each Chief Cashier, beginning with C. P. Mahon. Certain notes have not yet been traced and indeed may not exist (early replacements, for example). The author is loath to alter a numbering system that is now so firmly established. Collectors will, however, find some adjustments in the numbering of D. H. F. Somerset notes to accommodate issues made after the last edition of *English Paper Money* was published in 1984.

CYRIL PATRICK MAHON
(1925–1929)
(The 18th Chief Cashier)

Author's collection

Patrick Mahon was born on 9 September 1882 and was elected to the Bank on 14 March 1901. He was Chief Cashier from 1 April 1925 to 26 March 1929 and Comptroller from 1929–32 when he was forced to retire due to ill health. He died in 1945.

1928 (22 November) TEN SHILLINGS

			EF	VF
B210	**10s.**	Red-brown		
		Prefix coding: Letter, number, number.		
		Quantity printed: 410 million.		
		Serial letters:		
		A 01 (one million notes of the inaugural run)	450	250
		Z - - (first series traced from Z01)	145	50
		Y - -, X - -, W- -	115	40
		V - - (last series traced to V11)	500	250
B211	**10s.**	Red-brown replacement note		
		Prefix coding: Not known.		
		Quantity printed: Not known.		
		Serial letter: Probably handset.	—	—

1928 (22 November) ONE POUND

			EF	VF
B21~~1~~	**£1**	Green		
		Prefix coding: Letter, number, number.		
		Quantity printed: 725 million.		
		Serial letters:		
		A 01 (one million notes of the inaugural run)	350	200
		A - - (first series traced from A02)	75	40
		B - -, C - -, D - -, E - -, F - -, G - -	60	25
		H - - (last series traced to H32)	125	60

MAHON (contd.)

B213 **£1**   Green replacement note
Prefix coding: Not known.
Quantity printed: Not known.   —   —
Serial letter: Probably handset.

B214   £1 and 10s. notes with matching serial numbers in
presentation parchment envelope inscribed "Bank of
England 22 November 1928". Only 100 pairs are believed
to have been issued, carrying the first 100 serial
numbers.   Price (*EF*) from 2,750

1925

Large denomination notes from FIVE POUNDS to ONE THOUSAND POUNDS
bearing various dates between 1925 and 1929 were issued with the signature of C. P. Mahon. The notes were of the traditional design and
dimensions, measuring $8\frac{3}{8} \times 5\frac{5}{16}$in. They were plate-printed in pairs, at St.
Luke's Works, Old Street, London, then cut leaving one straight edge and
three deckled edges. The paper was made by Portals Ltd. Notes of £10 and
above were legal tender until 1 May 1945 and £5 notes without metal
thread were legal tender until 1 March 1946—no doubt to allow wartime
hoarders more time to pay them in.

			EF	VF
B215	**£5**	Black on white (from 1 April 1925)	145	70
B216	**£10**	Black on white	225	100
B217	**£20**	Black on white	700	400
B218	**£50**	Black on white	700	400
B219	**£100**	Black on white	1,250	650
B220	**£200**	Black on white	—	—
B221	**£500**	Black on white	—	—
B222	**£1,000**	Black on white	—	—

For prefix details and dates of Mahon £5 notes see Appendix B.

Mahon branch notes were issued (£5 in ascending order of rarity) from the
following eight offices:

1. MANCHESTER   5. BIRMINGHAM
2. LEEDS   6. NEWCASTLE
3. HULL   7. PLYMOUTH
4. LIVERPOOL   8. BRISTOL

Collectors should be aware that 01 (or other) first prefixes, linking prefixes
and closing prefixes are likely to command a premium in EF grade.
For classification of specimen notes and errors see pages 140–145.

MAHON (contd.)

B215 – Hull

B216

B217 – Manchester

B219

MAHON (contd.)

B221

B222

© Bank of England

BASIL GAGE CATTERNS
(1929–1934)
(The 19th Chief Cashier)

Basil Catterns was born in 1886 at Oswaldtwistle in Lancashire, the son of the Rector, the Rev. T. E. S. Catterns. He was educated at Trent College, Derbyshire and after five years with the Manchester & Liverpool District Banking Company (later the District Bank) at Accrington, he entered Bank service on 13 February 1908. During the First World War he served as a Second Lieutenant in the Royal Field Artillery but was severely wounded in the legs in 1917. In 1920 he settled permanently in the Chief Cashier's office; he became Assistant Chief in 1923, Deputy Chief in April 1925 and succeeded Patrick Mahon as Chief Cashier on 27 March 1929. He held this post until 17 April 1934, when he was appointed an Executive Director. In March 1936 he succeeded Sir Ernest Harvey as Deputy Governor and retired in 1945, serving two more years as a non-executive Director. He died on 5 February 1969.

1930 (15 July) TEN SHILLINGS

Design, watermark and dimensions as for C. P. Mahon notes. Printed at St. Luke's Works, London.

			EF	*VF*
B223	**10s.**	Red-brown		
		Prefix coding: Letter, number, number.		
		Quantity printed: 965 million.		
		Serial letters:		
		V - - (series traced from V14)	75	40
		U - -, T - -, S - -, R - -, O - -, N - -, M - -, L - -	45	20
		K - - (last series traced to K99)	60	25
B224	**10s.**	Red-brown replacement note		
		Prefix coding: Not known.		
		Quantity printed: Not known.		
		Serial letter: Probably handset.	—	—

CATTERNS (contd.)

B223

1930 (15 July) ONE POUND

Design, watermark and dimensions as for C. P. Mahon notes. Printed at St.
Luke's Works, London.

			EF	VF
B225	£1	Green		
		Prefix coding: Letter, number, number.		
		Quantity printed: 1,450 million.		
		Serial letters:		
		H - - (first series traced from H33)	50	25
		J - -, K - -, L - -, M - -, N - -, O - -, R - -, S - -, T - -		
		U - -, W - -, X - -, Y —	30	15
		Z - - (last series traced to Z99)	45	25
B226	£1	Green		
		Prefix coding: Number, number, letter.		
		Quantity printed: 99 million.		
		Serial letter:		
		- - A (series traced from 01A to 99A)	125	65

EF   VF

B227 **£1**   Green replacement note
                  Prefix coding: Not known.
                  Quantity printed: Not known.
                  Serial letter: Probably handset.   —   —
Slight variations in the width of the design may be due to the use of different plates or to shrinkage of the paper.

1929

Large denomination notes from FIVE POUNDS to ONE THOUSAND POUNDS were issued bearing various dates between 1929 and 1934. Design, watermark and dimensions as for C. P. Mahon notes. Printed at St. Luke's Works, London.

			EF	VF
B228	**£5**	Black on white (from 30 March 1929)	125	60
B229	**£10**	Black on white	200	100
B230	**£20**	Black on white	525	275
B231	**£50**	Black on white	600	300
B232	**£100**	Black on white	950	400
B233	**£500**	Black on white	—	—
B234	**£1,000**	Black on white	—	—

For prefix details and dates of Catterns £5 notes see Appendix B.

B228 – Birmingham

CATTERNS (contd.)

Catterns branch notes were issued (£5 in ascending order of rarity) from the following eight offices:

1. LEEDS
2. MANCHESTER
3. HULL
4. LIVERPOOL

5. BIRMINGHAM
6. BRISTOL
7. NEWCASTLE
8. PLYMOUTH

B228 – Newcastle-on-Tyne (above), Plymouth (below)

B229 – Bristol

B232 – Bristol

CATTERNS (contd.)

B234

Collectors should be aware that 01 (or other) first prefixes, linking prefixes and closing prefixes are likely to command a premium in EF grade.

For classification of specimen notes and errors see pages 140–145.

KENNETH OSWALD PEPPIATT
(1934–1949)
(The 20th Chief Cashier)

© Bank of England

Kenneth Peppiatt was born in 1893. He was educated at Bancroft's School and was elected to the staff of the Bank on 9 November 1911. During the First World War he served with the 7th Batallion London Regiment, spending three years in Flanders. He rose to the rank of Major, was wounded twice and was awarded the M.C. and bar. Returning to the Bank after the war he rose to become Principal of the Discount Office in 1928 and Chief Cashier on 18 April 1934. KOP as he was known held the post for 15 years until 28 February 1949, the second longest period (after Gordon Nairne) in the century. He was knighted in 1941. From 1949 he was an Executive Director until his retirement in 1957 when he joined Coutts Bank as a Director. He died at the age of 90 on 12 May 1983.

FIRST PERIOD: 1934–1939

1934 (5 October) TEN SHILLINGS

Design, watermark and dimensions as for C. P. Mahon notes. Printed at St. Luke's Works, London.

			EF	*VF*
B235	**10s.**	Red-brown		
		Prefix-coding: Letter, number, number.		
		Quantity printed: 693 million.		
		Serial letters:		
		J -- (first series traced from J01)	70	35
		H--, E--, D--, C--, B--	55	25
		A-- (last series traced to A99)	60	30

PEPPIATT (contd.)

			EF	*VF*

B236 10s. Red-brown
Prefix coding: Number, number, letter.
Quantity printed: 850 million.
Serial letters:

- - Z (first series traced from 01Z)	65	30
- - Y , - - X , - - W , - - U , - - T , - - S , - - R	50	25
- - O (last series traced to 79O)	55	30

No examples have been found of notes with the serial letters --N and --M which were probably destroyed in the blitz of 1940.

B237 10s. Red-brown replacement note
Prefix coding: Not known.
Quantity printed: Not known.
Serial letter: Probably handset.   —   —

1934 (17 October) ONE POUND

Design, watermark and dimensions as for C. P. Mahon notes. Printed at St. Luke's Works, London.

B238 £1 Green
Prefix coding: Number, number, letter.
Quantity printed: 1,880 million.
Serial letters:

- - B (first series traced from 01B)	50	25
- - C , - - D , - - E , - - H , - - J , - - K , - - L , - - M , - - N ,		
- - O , - - R , - - S , - - T , - - V , - - W , - - X , - - Y	30	12
- - Z (last series traced to 99Z)	45	20

B239 £1 Green
Prefix coding: Letter, number, number, letter.
Quantity printed: 850 million.
Serial letters:

A - - A (first series traced from A03A)	40	20
B - - A , C - - A , D - - A , E - - A , H - - A , J - - A , K - - A	30	12
L - - A (last series traced to L39A)	45	20

No examples have been found of notes with the serial letters M--A, N--A and O--A which were probably destroyed in the blitz of 1940.

B240 £1 Green replacement note
Prefix coding: Not known.
Quantity printed: Not known.
Serial letters: Probably handset.   —   —

Slight variations in the width of the design may be due to the use of different plates or to shrinkage of the paper.

For classification of specimen notes and errors see pages 140–145.

B239(A) Guernsey overprint see page 88.

1934

Large denomination notes from FIVE POUNDS to ONE THOUSAND POUNDS, bearing various dates between 1934 and 1943. Design, watermark and dimensions as for C. P. Mahon. Printed at St. Luke's Works, London.

			EF	VF
B241	**£5**	Black on white (from 1 May 1934)	80	45
B242	**£10**	Black on white	135	75
B243	**£20**	Black on white	450	250
B244	**£50**	Black on white	500	275
B245	**£100**	Black on white	750	350
B246	**£500**	Black on white	from 4,000 (*VF*)	
B247	**£1,000**	Black on white	from 8,000 (*VF*)	

For prefix details and dates of Peppiatt £5 notes see Appendix B.

On 23 April 1943, the Chancellor of the Exchequer announced that the Bank would no longer issue notes of £10 and above. This was to counter the problems of hoarding and the dangers of forgery. The full story of the German forgeries carried out at Sachsenhausen concentration camp is told by Bryan Burke in his book *Nazi Counterfeiting of British Currency during World War II: Operation Andrew and Operation Bernhard.*

Peppiatt branch notes were issued (£5 in ascending order of rarity) from the following eight offices:

1. LIVERPOOL
2. MANCHESTER
3. LEEDS
4. BIRMINGHAM
5. NEWCASTLE
6. HULL
7. BRISTOL
8. PLYMOUTH

Collectors should be aware that 01 (or other) first prefixes, linking prefixes and closing prefixes are likely to command a premium in EF grade. For classification of specimen notes and errors see pages 140–145.

PEPPIATT (contd.)

B241 – Newcastle-on-Tyne

B241 – Bristol

B242 – Hull

B243 – Liverpool

PEPPIATT (contd.)

B244 – Birmingham

B245 – Manchester

B246 – Liverpool

B247

Most £100 and £500 notes that have come on to the market are from Liverpool. All branch notes were discontinued at the outbreak of war in 1939. The last recorded branch £5 note according to collector records came from Liverpool on 22 July 1938 and carries the prefix T/308.

PEPPIATT (contd.)

SECOND PERIOD: 1940–1948

1940 (29 March) ONE POUND

The blue emergency issue incorporating a metal thread—the invention of the General Manager of the Bank's printing works, Mr. S. B. Chamberlain. Basic design and dimensions unchanged, but a double line surrounded the unprinted part of the front containing the Britannia watermark. The notes were printed until September 1940 by offset-litho at St. Luke's Works, Old Street, London on banknote paper manufactured by Portals Ltd, and, thereafter, at Overton, Hampshire. Emergency issue £1 notes are legal tender until 28 May 1962.

			EF	VF
B248	**£1**	Pale blue (shades) *Prefix coding:* Letter, number, number, letter. *Quantity printed:* 297 million. *Serial letters:*		
		A - - D (first series traced from A 01D)	25	12
		A - - E (first series traced from A 01E)	20	8
		A - - H (first series traced from A 01H)	20	8

Originally these notes were thought to have been the ones printed by intaglio at the St. Luke's Works. It now seems doubtful whether this was the case, and it is possible some later prefixes were also printed there before the move to Overton. The classification is, however, being retained to avoid disrupting the numbering system.

B249	**£1**	Blue (shades) *Prefix coding:* Letter, number, number, letter. *Quantity printed:* 5,148 million. *Serial letters:*		
		B - - D, C - - D, D - - D, E - - D, H - - D, J - - D, K - - D, L - - D, M - - D, N - - D, O - - D, R - - D, S - - D, T - - D, U - - D, W - - D, X - - D, Y - - D	10	4
		Z - - D (last series traced to Z87D)	20	10
		B - - E, C - - E, D - - E, E - - E, H - - E, J - - E, K - - E, L - - E, M - - E, N - - E, O - - E, R - - E, S - - E, T - - E, U - - E	10	4
		W - - E (last series traced to W38E)	20	10
		B - - H, C - - H, D - - H, E - - H, H - - H, J - - H, K - - H, L - - H, M - - H, N - - H, O - - H, R - - H, S - - H, T - - H, U - - H, W - - H	10	4
		X - - H (last series traced to X94H)	20	10

B250	**£1**	Blue replacement note *Prefix coding:* Not known. *Quantity printed:* Not known. *Serial letters:* Probably handset.		

B249

Some notes on shading: St. Luke's Works was hit by two bombs on the night of 9/10 September 1940 and production of banknotes was then transferred to emergency premises near the Bank's paper suppliers, Portals, at Overton in Hampshire. The wide variety of shades to be found in the £1 notes is the result of wartime conditions when it was extremely difficult to obtain certain types of ink. Thus at least 20 combinations of colour may be identified.

Obverse main design
Pale blue
Blue
Deep blue (ultramarine)

Obverse signature block
Light shading
Medium shading
Heavy shading

Obverse background
Pink
Deep pink
Buff

Reverse
Pale blue
Pale blue
Greenish-blue

1940 (2 April) TEN SHILLINGS

The mauve emergency issue incorporated a metal thread as in the blue £1. Basic design and dimensions were unchanged. Printed until September 1940 by offset-litho at St. Luke's Works, Old Street, London, on banknote paper manufactured by Portals Ltd. Thereafter at Overton, Hampshire. Emergency issue 10s. notes were legal tender until 29 October 1962.

PEPPIATT (contd.)

			EF	VF
B251	**10s.**	Mauve (shades)		

Prefix coding: Letter, number, number, letter.
Quantity printed: 2,200 million.
Serial letters:

	EF	VF
Z - - D (first series traced from Z01D)	30	15
Y - - D , X - - D , W - - D , U - - D , T - - D , S - - D , R - - D , O - - D , N - - D		
M - - D , L - - D , K - - D , J - - D , H - - D , E - - D , D - - D , C - - D , B - - D	25	10
A - - D (last series traced to A86D)	30	15
Z - - E (first series traced from Z01E)	30	10
Y - - E	30	10
X - - E (last series traced to X21E)	80	45

B252	**10s.**	Mauve replacement note

Prefix coding: Not known.
Quantity printed: Not known.
Serial letters: Probably handset.   — —

Slight variations in the width of the design may be due to the use of
different plates or to shrinkage of the paper. The colour of the ink used also
varies considerably and a pleasing display can be made up of shades from
dull mauve to light violet.

1941 (date unknown) FIVE SHILLINGS and HALF-CROWN

The emergency small-denomination notes of five shillings and half-crown
were prepared by the Bank of England on instructions of the government
which feared there might be difficulties in transporting coinage. The notes,
which were printed on unwatermarked paper with the design on both sides,
incorporate a metal thread and measure 114mm × 73mm ($4\frac{1}{2}$ × $2\frac{7}{8}$in.).
Although they were distributed to the clearing banks, the notes were never
issued to the public and were destroyed in the late 1940s. Examples which
survive have no serial numbers.

B253	**5s.**	Olive-green (design) on pale pink (background)

Prefix coding: None.
Quantity printed: Not known.
Serial letters: None.   3,500 1,500

                                                             EF   VF
B254 **2s.6d.** Black (design) on pale blue (background)
               Prefix coding: None.
               Quantity printed: Not known.
               Serial letters: None.   3,500 1,500

1945 FIVE POUNDS

Design and dimensions as for C. P. Mahon, but metal thread is now
incorporated, the paper is thicker and heavier, a new serial numbering
system is brought in and the watermark shows five figures instead of four.
The notes were printed at St. Luke's Works, Old Street, London and were
legal tender until 13 March 1961. Although they were not issued until 1945,
many notes have 1944 dates.

                                                             EF   VF
B255 **£5**   Black on white
               Prefix coding: Letter, number, number.
               Quantity printed: 40 million.
               Serial letters:
                  E -- (series traced from E01 dated 2 Sept. 1944)   75   40
                  H--, J --, K--   60   35
                  L -- (series traced to L02 dated 12 Dec. 1945)   125   60
For prefix details and dates see Appendix B.
     Collectors should be aware that 01 (or other) first prefixes, linking
prefixes and closing prefixes are likely to command a premium in EF grade.
     For classification of specimen notes and errors see pages 140–145.

THE STATES OF GUERNSEY OVERPRINTS

When the Germans occupied the Channel Islands in the Second World War,
German money was made legal tender. As a result almost all British and
Channel Islands currency 'disappeared under the floorboards'. Because of
the shortage of small change the Guernsey authorities obtained permission

PEPPIATT (contd.)

from the Germans in 1941 to issue small denominations of 6d., 1s.3d., 2s.6d. and 5s. The Germans agreed subject to the withdrawal of £5,000 worth of Guernsey £1 notes which was done by handing over soiled notes being held for destruction, but not before they had been overprinted front and back "Withdrawn from circulation" with the date.

When these emergency low denomination notes also began to run short, agreement was obtained for a further issue of £5,000 except that this time the Germans demanded that £5,000 of Bank of England notes should be withdrawn. Again the notes were overprinted. After the liberation in 1945 £2,000 of these notes were discovered in Jersey and returned to the Bank of England. The balance came to light in the early 1980s and were sold to collectors, mostly in the U.S.A.

The notes involved are the green unthreaded £1 signed by Mahon, Catterns and Peppiatt and the blue wartime £1. The overprints (front and back) read:

<table>
<tr><td>Withdrawn from
Circulation
September 18th,
1941.</td><td>or</td><td>Withdrawn from
Circulation
November 10th
1941.</td></tr>
</table>

The majority of notes are printed with a full stop after the year on the front but no full stop on the back (type A); some have a full stop on the front and the back (type B); some have a full stop on the back but not on the front (type C). For illustration see page 79.

Recorded prefixes and quantities are:

	September 18th, 1941	*EF*	*VF*
B212(A) Mahon	A, B, C, D, E, F, G, H (total number = 48)	450	250
B225(A) Catterns	H, J, K, L, M, N, O, R, S, T, U, W, X, Y, Z (total number = 69)	375	250
B226(A) Catterns	A (total number = 5)	from 450 (*EF*)	
B238(A) Peppiatt	B, C, D, E, H, J, K, L, M, N, O, R, S, T, U, W, X, Y, Z (total number = 330)	300	125
B239(A) Peppiatt (Pre-war)	A--A, B--A, C--A, D--A, E--A, H--A, J--A, K--A, L--A (total number = 1,885)	200	100
B248(A) Peppiatt (Blue)	A--D (total number = 35)	400	225
B249(A) Peppiatt (Blue)	C--D (total number = 85)	375	200
	November 10th, 1941		
B239(B) Peppiatt (Pre-war)	E03A only (stop front and back) (total number = 75)	400	225
B239(C) Peppiatt (Pre-war)	E15A only (no stop front, stop reverse) (total number = 403)	325	150

All the serial numbers of the notes have been recorded as a precaution against forgery of the overprints.

THIRD PERIOD 1948

1948 (17 June) TEN SHILLINGS

Reissue of the unthreaded pre-war notes. This enabled the Bank of England to use up stockpiled notes and supplies of paper without the metal thread. The design, dimensions and watermark were the same as for C. P. Mahon notes and they were printed at St. Luke's Works, London.

			EF	VF
B256	**10s.**	Red-brown		
		Prefix coding: Number, number, letter.		
		Quantity printed: 65 million.		
		Serial letter:		
		- - L (series traced from 05L to 71L)	65	30

The serials of this issue overlap with those of the Peppiatt threaded 10s. (B262).

B257	**10s.**	Red-brown replacement note		
		Prefix coding: Not known.		
		Quantity printed: Not known.		
		Serial letter: Probably handset.	—	—

1948 (17 June) ONE POUND

Reissue of the unthreaded pre-war notes. This enabled the Bank of England to use up stockpiled notes and supplies of paper without the metal thread. The design, dimensions and watermark were the same as for C. P. Mahon notes and they were printed at St. Luke's Works, London.

B258	**£1**	Green		
		Prefix coding: Letter, number, number, letter.		
		Quantity printed: 140 million.		
		Serial letters:		
		R - - A (first series traced from R01A)	30	12
		S - - A (last series traced to S48A)	35	15

The S--A serials of this issue overlap with those of the Peppiatt threaded £1 (B260)

B259	**£1**	Green replacement note		
		Prefix coding: Not known.		
		Quantity printed: Not known.		
		Serial letters: Probably handset.	—	—

PEPPIATT (contd.)

Slight variations in the width of the design may be due to the use of different plates or to shrinkage of the paper.

Collectors should be aware that 01 (or other) first prefixes, linking prefixes and closing prefixes are likely to command a premium in EF grade.

For classification of specimen notes and errors see pages 140–145.

FOURTH PERIOD 1948–1949

1948 (13 September) ONE POUND

It took little more than three months to use up the supply of pre-war unthreaded paper, whereupon the Bank reverted to the newer threaded variety. The notes were printed at St. Luke's Works, London.

			EF	VF
B260	£1	Green		

Prefix coding: Letter, number, number, letter.
Quantity printed: 1,190 million.
Serial letters:

	EF	VF
S - - A (first series traced from S40A)	35	12
T - - A , U - - A , W - - A , X - - A , Y - - A	14	5
Z - - A (last series traced to Z99A)	16	5
A - - B (first series traced from A01B)	16	5
B - - B , C - - B , D - - B , E - - B	12	4
H - - B (last series traced to H36B)	25	10

The serials of this issue overlap with those of the Peppiatt unthreaded £1 (B258).

			EF	VF
B261	**£1**	Green replacement note		

Prefix coding: Letter, number, number, letter.
Quantity printed: 9 million.
Serial letters:

		EF	VF
S - - S (series traced from S01S to S09S)		160	80

1948 (25 October) TEN SHILLINGS

It took little more than four months to use up the supply of pre-war unthreaded paper, whereupon the Bank reverted to the newer threaded variety. The notes were printed at St. Luke's Works, London.

B262 **10s.** Red-brown

Prefix coding: Number, number, letter.
Quantity printed: 420 million.
Serial letter:

	EF	VF
- - L (first series traced from 71L)	160	80
- - K , - - J , - - H	20	8
- - E (last series traced to 91E)	35	15

The --L serials of this issue may overlap with those of the Peppiatt unthreaded 10s. (B256).

PEPPIATT (contd.)

EF   VF

B263 10s.   Red-brown replacement note
Prefix coding: Number, number, letter.
Quantity printed: 3 million.
Serial letter:

- - A (series traced from 01A to 03A)   350   250

Slight variations in the width of the design may be due to the use of
different plates or to shrinkage of the paper.

1948 FIVE POUNDS

Design, watermark and dimensions as for K. O. Peppiatt £5 notes of the
second period (B255), except that much thinner paper is used. All notes are
dated 1947 and were printed at St. Luke's Works, London. They were not,
however, issued until 1948.

B264 £5   Black on white
Prefix coding: Letter, number, number.
Quantity printed: 17 million.
Serial letters:

L - - (series traced from L03 dated 1 Jan. 1947)   60   35
M - - (series traced to M71 dated 16 July 1947)   65   35

For prefix details and dates see Appendix B.

For classification of specimen notes and errors see pages 140–145.

Collectors should be aware that 01 (or other) first prefixes, linking
prefixes and closing prefixes are likely to command a premium in EF grade.

PEPPIATT SUMMARISED:

The four note issuing periods of Kenneth Peppiatt can be somewhat
confusing, especially for new collectors, so for convenience the main types
are summarised here:

TEN
SHILLINGS: Type 1   Pre-war   Letter, number, number (unthreaded)
Type 2a Pre-war   Number, number, letter (unthreaded)
Type 2b Post-war Number, number, letter (unthreaded)
Type 3   Wartime   Letter, number, number, letter (threaded)
Type 4   Post-war Number, number, letter (threaded)

ONE
POUND: Type 1   Pre-war   Number, number, letter (unthreaded)
Type 2a Pre-war   Letter, number, number, letter (unthreaded)
Type 2b Post-war Letter, number, number, letter (unthreaded)
Type 3   Wartime   Letter, number, number, letter (threaded)
Type 4   Post-war Letter, number, number, letter (threaded)

© Bank of England

PERCIVAL SPENCER BEALE (1949–1955)
(The 21st Chief Cashier)

Percival Beale was born on 14 September 1906 and entered Bank service on 27 October 1924. He was Chief Cashier from 1 March 1949 to 16 January 1955, when he retired. He died on 4 February 1981.

1950 (17 March) TEN SHILLINGS

Design, watermark and dimensions as for K. O. Peppiatt notes of the fourth period. Printed at St. Luke's Works, London.

			EF	VF
B265	**10s.**	Red-brown		
		Prefix coding: Number, number, letter.		
		Quantity printed: 307 million.		
		Serial letters:		
		- - E (first series traced from 92E)	150	75
		- - D , - - C	16	5
		- - B (last series traced to 99B)	16	5
B266	**10s.**	Red-brown		
		Prefix coding: Letter, number, number, letter.		
		Quantity printed: 1,668 million.		
		Serial letters:		
		Z - - Z (first series traced from Z 01Z)	25	10
		Y - - Z , X - - Z , W - - Z , U - - Z , T - - Z , S - - Z , R - - Z , O - - Z ,		
		N - - Z , M - - Z , L - - Z , K - - Z , J - - Z , H - - Z , E - - Z	16	5
		D - - Z (last series traced to D85Z)	25	10

BEALE (contd.)

			EF	VF
B267	**10s.**	Red-brown replacement note *Prefix coding:* Number, number, letter. *Quantity printed:* 30 million. *Serial letters:*		
		- - A (series traced from 04A to 35A)	80	40

1950 (17 March) ONE POUND

Design, watermark and dimensions as for K. O. Peppiatt notes of the fourth period. Printed at St. Luke's Works, London.

			EF	VF
B268	**£1**	Green *Prefix coding:* Letter, number, number, letter. *Quantity printed:* 4,275 million. *Serial letters:*		
		H - - B (first series traced from H37B)	16	8
		J - - B , K - - B , L - - B , M - - B , N - - B , O - - B , R - - B ,		
		S - - B , T - - B , U - - B , W - - B , X - - B , Y - - B	6	3
		Z - - B (last series traced to Z99B)	12	5
		A - - C (first series traced from A01C)	12	5
		B - - C , C - - C , D - - C , E - - C , H - - C , J - - C , K - - C ,		
		L - - C , M - - C , N - - C , O - - C , R - - C , S - - C , T - - C ,		
		U - - C , W - - C , X - - C , Y - - C	6	3
		Z - - C (last series traced to Z99C)	12	5
		A - - J (first series traced from A01J)	12	5
		B - - J , C - - J , D - - J , E - - J , H - - J , J - - J , K - - J	6	3
		L - - J (last series traced to L63J)	16	8

B269

B269 **£1** Green replacement note
Prefix coding: Letter, number, number, letter.
Quantity printed: 60 million.
Serial letters:
    S - - S (series traced from S10S to S70S)   40   15

Slight variations in the width of the design may be due to the use of different plates or to shrinkage of the paper.

1949 FIVE POUNDS

Design, watermark and dimensions as for K. O. Peppiatt notes of the fourth period (B264). Printed at St. Luke's Works, London.

B270 **£5** Black on white
Prefix coding: Letter, number, number.
Quantity printed: Not known.
Serial letters:

	EF	VF
M - - (series traced from M72 dated 1 March 1949)	65	35
N - -, O - -, P - -, R - -, S - -, T - -, U - -, V - -, W - -, X - -	50	30
Y - - (series traced to Y70 dated 27 Aug. 1952)	65	35

For prefix details and dates see Appendix B.

Collectors should be aware that 01 (or other) first prefixes, linking prefixes and closing prefixes are likely to command a premium in EF grade.

For classification of specimen notes and errors see pages 140–145.

BEALE (contd.)

SERIES B (HELMETED BRITANNIA) UNISSUED

It should not be thought that the Bank of England were lacking in ideas for designs to replace the 1928 issue. In June 1931, Kruger Gray, Frederick Griggs and Stephen Gooden were invited to compete for new note designs, although Gooden's winning entry was never taken up. During the 1930s Gooden completed a number of other designs for the 10s. and £1 notes, including a 10s. featuring St. George and the Dragon, and a £1 note showing a bare-headed Britannia holding a spear.

Then in the late 1940s and early 1950s Gooden produced two further series of notes. One of these depicted Sir John Houblon, the first Governor of the Bank, and was known as the "Houblon" series. It will be interesting to see whether any of Gooden's ideas are adopted in the design of the £50 series E note due in 1994 to mark the Bank's tercentenary. Gooden's other design was selected for issue and was officially classified as series B. On the obverse of the notes there is a vignette of Britannia in her helmet and the reverses of all three denominations, including the issued £5, show three variations of the lion and key motif on a multicoloured background.

Sadly Gooden himself did not live to see the issue of the £5 in February 1957 (with the signature of O'Brien). This note was already in production when it was announced in July 1956 that H.M. The Queen had consented to her portrait appearing on Bank of England notes. As a result plans to bring in the series B 10s. and £1 were shelved, and Gooden's successor, Robert Austin, set to work on the series C (Portrait) notes.

For further information see *In Search of Stephen Gooden* by John Deacon in *The Old Lady of Threadneedle Street* September 1980. Also *The Search for the Inimitable Note* by Clive Goodacre in *Penrose 1982*, the international review of the graphic arts. The latter also contains much of interest relating to the series D (Pictorial) notes.

© Bank of England

LESLIE KENNETH O'BRIEN (1955–1962)
(The 22nd Chief Cashier)

Leslie O'Brien was born on 8 February 1908 and entered Bank service in 1927. He was private secretary to the Governor for two years which included the last year of Lord Norman's term and the first year of Lord Catto's. He was appointed Deputy Chief Cashier in 1951 and was Chief Cashier from 17 January 1955 to 28 February 1962. He became an Executive Director in 1962 and Deputy Governor from 1964–66. His term as Governor lasted from 1966–73 and he was the first member of the Bank's ordinary staff to obtain this top position. He was knighted in 1967 and became Lord O'Brien of Lothbury in 1973.

FIRST PERIOD: SERIES A (BRITANNIA) 1955–60

1955 (21 November) TEN SHILLINGS

Design, watermark and dimensions as for K. O. Peppiatt notes of the fourth period. Printed at St. Luke's Works, London.

			EF	*VF*
B271	**10s.**	Red-brown		
		Prefix coding: Letter, number, number, letter.		
		Quantity printed: 2,500 million.		
		Serial letters:		
		D - - Z (first series traced from D86Z)	50	25
		C - - Z , B - - Z	15	5
		A - - Z (last series traced to A95Z)	18	6
		Z - - Y (first series traced from Z01Y)	18	6
		Y - - Y , X - - Y , W - - Y , U - - Y , T - - Y , S - - Y , R - - Y , O - - Y , N - - Y ,		
		M - - Y , L - - Y , K - - Y , J - - Y , H - - Y , E - - Y , D - - Y , C - - Y , B - - Y	12	5
		A - - Y (last series traced to A99Y)	18	6
		Z - - X (first series traced from Z01X)	18	6
		Y - - X (last series traced to Y25X)	30	10

O'BRIEN *(contd.)*

			EF	VF
B272	**10s.**	Red-brown replacement note		

Prefix coding: Number, number, letter.
Quantity printed: 32 million.
Serial letters:
- - A (series traced from 36A to 68A)   80   40

B273 **£1**   Green
Prefix coding: Letter, number, number, letter.
Quantity printed: 3,900 million.
Serial letters:

	EF	VF
L - - J (first series traced from L64J)	15	5
M - - J , N - - J , O - - J , R - - J , S - - J , T - - J , U - - J , W - - J , X - - J , Y - - J	6	3
Z - - J (last series traced to Z99J)	10	4
A - - K (first series traced from A01K)	10	4
B - - K , C - - K , D - - K , E - - K , H - - K , J - - K , K - - K , L - - K , M - - K , N - - K , O - - K , R - - K , S - - K , T - - K , U - - K , W - - K , X - - K , Y - - K	6	3
Z - - K (last series traced to Z99K)	10	4
A - - L (first series traced from A02L)	10	4
B - - L , C - - L , D - - L , E - - L , H - - L , J - - L	6	3
K - - L (last series traced to K13L)	50	25

B274 **£1**   Green replacement note
Prefix coding: Letter, number, number, letter.
Quantity printed: 51 million.
Serial letters:

	EF	VF
S - - S (series traced from S71S to S98S)	40	8
S - - T (series traced from S01T to S21T)	55	10

B274

1955 FIVE POUNDS

Design, watermark and dimensions as for K. O. Peppiatt notes of the fourth period (B264). Printed at St. Luke's Works, London.

			EF	*VF*
B275	**£5**	Black on white		
		Prefix coding: Letter, number, number.		
		Quantity printed: Not known.		
		Serial letters:		
		Y - - (series traced from Y71 dated 17 Jan. 1955)	70	35
		Z - - (series traced to Z99 dated 15 June 1955)	70	35
B276	**£5**	Black on white		
		Prefix coding: Letter, number, number, letter.		
		Quantity printed: Not known.		
		Serial letters:		
		A - - A (series traced from A01A dated 16 June 1955)	65	35
		B - - A , C - - A	60	35
		D - - A (series traced to D99A dated 20 Sept. 1956)	70	35

For prefix details and dates see Appendix B.

Collectors should be aware that 01 (or other) first prefixes, linking prefixes and closing prefixes are likely to command a premium in EF grade.

For classification of specimen notes and errors see pages 140–145.

O'BRIEN (contd.)

SECOND PERIOD: SERIES B (HELMETED BRITANNIA) 1957–67

1957 (21 February) FIVE POUNDS

Designed by Stephen Gooden R.A. featuring on the obverse the helmeted head of Britannia, and on the reverse the lion and key (for further details of the B series as a whole see page 96). Plate-printed in sheets of 21 at St. Luke's Works, London, on banknote paper manufactured by Portals Ltd. with watermark incorporating the helmeted head of Britannia. The notes measure 158.7mm × 75.5mm (6¼ × 3½in.) and were legal tender until 27 June 1967. In a letter to the author in 1989 the Bank has revealed for the first time that a total of 649 million Series B £5 notes was issued. Quantities printed for each prefix are the author's unofficial estimate and must be regarded as approximate.

			EF	VF
B277	**£5**	Blue, pale green and orange (shaded symbol)		
		Prefix coding: Letter, number, number.		
		Quantity printed: 406 million.		
		Serial letters:		
		A -- (first series traced from A01)	25	10
		B --, C --, D --	15	8
		E -- (last series traced to E06)	40	20

Originally the series was thought to end in H--, but there seems to have been confusion between the two types, and there is so far no proven sighting of an H-- prefix with shaded £5 symbols.

B278   **£1**   Multicoloured (blue and lilac predominating)
                Never issued.

B279   **10s.**   Multicoloured (purple and orange predominating)
                Never issued.

1961 (12 July) FIVE POUNDS

Design, watermark and dimensions as B277 above except that the £5 symbols on the reverse are printed in outline only instead of shaded in dark blue. Printed at the Bank of England Works, Loughton, Essex.

B280   £5   Blue, pale green and orange (white symbol)
                Prefix coding: Letter, number, number.
                Quantity printed: 243 million.
                Serial letters:

		EF	VF
H -- (first series traced from H01)		25	10
J --		15	8
K -- (last series traced to K45)		35	15

Collectors should be aware that 01 (or other) first prefixes, linking prefixes ⁷8d closing prefixes are likely to command a premium in EF grade.

For classification of specimen notes and errors see pages 140–145.

THIRD PERIOD: SERIES C (PORTRAIT) 1960–1979

Stephen Gooden died on 21 September 1955 and was replaced by Robert Austin R.A. Professor of Engraving at the Royal College of Art and President of both the Royal Society of Painters in Watercolours and the Royal Society of Painter-Etchers and Engravers.

In July 1956 it was announced that H.M. The Queen had consented to her portrait appearing on Bank of England notes, and on 19 November 1959 the Bank announced that the new £1 note would be issued in 1960. It was to be part of a new Series C with denominations up to £10.

The £1 and 10s. notes which were designed by Robert Austin, incorporate the Queen's portrait in a complex blend of machine-engraved geometric patterns, and on the reverse the figure of Britannia seated. The notes were initially printed intaglio in sheets of 24 (3 × 8) at the Bank of England Works, Loughton, Essex, on banknote paper manufactured by Portals Ltd., with watermark of continuous laureate head.

However, in 1961 experimental £1 notes were produced in sheets of 21 (7 × 3) on a new reel-fed press, developed by Masson, Scott, Thrissell Engineering Ltd. of Bristol, in conjunction with the Bank's own engineers. To identify them from other notes in circulation they had a small capital letter 'R' (standing for Research) on the reverse and were prefixed A01N, A05N and A06N (see B283).

Portrait £1 notes measure 151mm × 71.8mm (6 × 2¼in.) and were legal tender until 31 May 1979. Portrait 10s. notes measure 140mm × 66.7mm (5½ × 2⅝in.) and were legal tender until 22 November 1970. In a letter to the author in 1989 the Bank has revealed for the first time that a total of 3,759 million Series C 10s. and 20,350 million £1 notes were issued. Quantities

O'BRIEN (contd.)

printed for each prefix are the author's unofficial estimate and must be regarded as approximate within the overall total.

1960 (17 March) ONE POUND

			EF	VF
B281	£1	Green		

Prefix coding: Letter, number, number.
Quantity printed: 1,782 million.
Serial letters:

	EF	VF
A -- (first series traced from A01)	9	3
B--, C--, D--, E--, H--, J--, K--, L--,		
N--, R--, S--, T--, U--, W--, X--, Y--	4	—
Z -- (last series traced to Z99)	9	3

B282 £1   Green
Prefix coding: Number, number, letter.
Quantity printed: 1,782 million.
Serial letters:

	EF	VF
--A (first series traced from 01A)	9	3
--B, --C, --D, --E, --H, --J, --K, --L,		
--N, --R, --S, --T, --U, --W, --X, --Y	4	—
--Z (last series traced to 99Z)	9	3

B283 £1   Green experimental note
Prefix coding: Letter, number, number, letter.
Quantity printed: 6 million (3 million issued)
Serial letters:

	EF	VF
A -- N (series traced in A01N, A05N and A06N only)	175	60

Notes with A01N have a long tail to the 'R' whereas those with A05N and A06N have a short-tailed 'R'. A05N is the scarcest prefix of the three. So far no examples of notes bearing the prefixes A02N, A03N and A04N have come to light.

			EF	VF

B284 **£1**   Green
Prefix coding: Letter, number, number, letter.
Quantity printed: 76 million.
Serial letters:
   B - - N (series traced from B01N to B76N)   20   5

B285 **£1**   Green replacement note
Prefix coding: Letter, number, number.
Quantity printed: 66 million.
Serial letter:
   M - - (series traced from M01 to M68)   20   5

1963 (4 April) TEN SHILLINGS

Design, watermark and dimensions as detailed above. Printed at the Bank
of England Works, Loughton, Essex.

B286 **10s.**   Red-brown
Prefix coding: Letter, number, number.
Quantity printed: 756 million.
Serial letters:
   A - - (first series traced from A01)   10   3
   B - -, C - -, D - -, E - -, H - -, J - -   4   —
   K - - (last series traced to K64)   12   3

B287 **10s.**   Red-brown replacement note
Prefix coding: Letter, number, number.
Quantity printed: 18 million.
Serial letter:
   M - - (series traced from M01 to M18)   35   15

Collectors should be aware that 01 (or other) first prefixes, linking prefixes
and closing prefixes are likely to command a premium in EF grade.

For classification of specimen notes and errors see pages 140–145.

B286

© Bank of England

JASPER QUINTUS HOLLOM
(1962–1966)
(The 23rd Chief Cashier)

Jasper Hollom was born on 16 December 1917. His first job at the age of 17 was an insurance clerk, but in 1936 he entered Bank service. During the war he served in the infantry in the Middle East and the Western Desert but was captured in 1942 and sent to a prisoner of war camp in Italy. He rejoined the Bank after the war and worked as assistant to the Chief Cashier, Leslie O'Brien. In 1956 he was made Deputy Chief Cashier and was Chief Cashier from 1 March 1962 to 30 June 1966. A press comment at the time said: "Hollom has a certain dignified ring to it that seems wholly British and most reassuring—there could never be the slightest doubt that Mr. Hollom would pay the bearer on demand the sum of one pound". He was appointed to the Court of Directors in 1966 and succeeded Sir Maurice Parsons as Deputy Governor in March 1970, a position he held until 1980. He was knighted in 1975. Sir Jasper Hollom retired on 29 February 1984 after serving a further four years as a non-executive Director.

1963 (27 February) ONE POUND

Design, watermark and dimensions as for L. K. O'Brien series C notes. Plate-printed at the Bank of England Works, Loughton, Essex. Some notes (B292 and B293) carry a small capital letter 'G' on the reverse indicating that they were printed on an experimental German Goebel press.

			EF	*VF*
B288	£1	Green		
		Prefix coding: Letter, number, number, letter.		
		Quantity printed: 5,875 million.		
		Serial letters:		
		B - - N (first series traced from B77N)	55	25
		C - - N , D - - N , E - - N , H - - N , J - - N , K - - N , L - - N		
		A - - R , B - - R , C - - R , D - - R , E - - R , H - - R , J - - R , K - - R , L - - R		
		A - - S , B - - S , C - - S , D - - S , E - - S , H - - S , J - - S , K - - S , L - - S		
		A - - T , B - - T , C - - T , ** , E - - T , H - - T , J - - T , K - - T , L - - T	4	—
		A - - U , B - - U , C - - U , D - - U , E - - U , H - - U , J - - U , K - - U , L - - U		
		A - - X , B - - X , C - - X , D - - X , E - - X , H - - X , J - - X , K - - X , **		
		A - - W , B - - W , ** , D - - W , E - - W , H - - W , J - - W , K - - W , L - - W		
		A - - Y		
		B - - Y (last series traced to B11Y)	55	25
	**	For prefix gaps see 'G' notes under B292 below.		
B289	£1	Green replacement note		
		Prefix coding: Letter, number, number.		
		Quantity printed: 32 million.		
		Serial letter:		
		M - - (series traced from M68 to M99)	30	15
B290	£1	Green replacement note		
		Prefix coding: Number, number, letter.		
		Quantity printed: 99 million.		
		Serial letter:		
		- - M (series traced from 01M to 99M)	15	8
B291	£1	Green replacement note		
		Prefix coding: Letter, number, number, letter.		
		Quantity printed: 8 million.		
		Serial letters:		
		M - - R (series traced from M01R to M08R)	30	15

HOLLOM (contd.)

			EF	VF
B292	**£1**	Green (printed on a Goebel machine)		
		Prefix coding: Letter, number, number, letter.		
		Quantity printed: 387 million.		
		Serial letters ('G' reverse):		
		A - - N (first series traced from A09N)	12	5
		D - - T , C - - W	6	—
		L - - X (last series traced to L99X)	6	—
B293	**£1**	Green replacement note (printed on a Goebel machine)		
		Prefix coding: Letter, number, number, letter.		
		Quantity printed: 28 million.		
		Serial letters ('G' reverse):		
		M - - N (series traced from M01N to M28N)	15	8

1963 (4 April) TEN SHILLINGS

Design, watermark and dimensions as for L. K. O'Brien Series C notes. Printed at the Bank of England Works, Loughton, Essex.

			EF	VF
B294	**10s.**	Red-brown		
		Prefix coding: Letter, number, number.		
		Quantity printed: 1,025 million.		
		Serial letters:		
		K - - (first series traced from K65)	15	5
		L - - , N - - , R - - , S - - , T - - , U - - , W - - , X - - , Y - -	4	—
		Z - - (last series traced to Z99)	10	4
B295	**10s.**	Red-brown		
		Prefix coding: Number, number, letter.		
		Quantity printed: 1,015 million.		
		Serial letters:		
		- - A (first series traced from 01A)	10	4
		- - B , - - C , - - D , - - E , - - H , - - J , - - K , - - L , - - N	4	—
		- - R (last series traced to 26R)	25	10
B296	**10s.**	Red-brown replacement note		
		Prefix coding: Letter, number, number.		
		Quantity printed: 34 million.		
		Serial letter:		
		M - - (series traced from M19 to M55)	30	10

1963 (21 February) FIVE POUNDS

Designed by Reynolds Stone, C.B.E., R.D.I. as the third in the Portrait Series C notes, featuring the Queen's portrait on the obverse and the figure of a child Britannia (modelled by the artist's daughter) on the reverse. Plate-printed in sheets of 18 (6 × 3) at the Bank of England Works, Loughton, Essex, on banknote paper manufactured by Portals Ltd., with watermark of continuous laureate head. The notes measure 140mm × 84.8mm ($5\frac{1}{2}$ × $3\frac{5}{16}$in.) and were legal tender until 31 August 1973. In a letter to the author in 1989 the Bank has revealed for the first time that a total of 2,200 million Series C £5 notes were issued. Quantities printed for each prefix are the author's unofficial estimate and must be regarded as approximate within the overall total.

			EF	VF
B297	£5	Blue		
		Prefix coding: Letter, number, number.		
		Quantity printed: 1,007 million.		
		Serial letters:		
		A -- (first series traced from A01)	20	14
		B --, C --, D --, E --, H --, J --, K --, L --, N--	15	10
		R -- (last series traced to R16)	30	15

B298	£5	Blue replacement note		
		Prefix coding: Letter, number, number.		
		Quantity printed: 7 million.		
		Serial letter:		
		M-- (series traced from M01 to M07)	65	30

HOLLOM (contd.)

1964 (21 February) TEN POUNDS

Designed by Reynolds Stone, C.B.E., R.D.I. as the fourth and final note in the Portrait Series C, featuring the Queen's portrait on the obverse together with a figure of Britannia seated and on the reverse a lion holding a key with the words 'Ten Pounds' in a scroll issuing from its mouth. Plate-printed in sheets of 15 (5 × 3) at the Bank of England Works, Loughton, Essex, on banknote paper manufactured by Portals Ltd., with watermark of the Queen's head. The notes measure 150mm × 93mm (5$\frac{7}{8}$ × 3$\frac{5}{8}$in.) and were legal tender until 31 May 1979. In a letter to the author in 1989 the Bank has revealed for the first time that a total of 250 million Series C £10 notes was issued. Quantities printed for each prefix are the author's unofficial estimate and must be regarded as approximate within the overall total.

			EF	VF
B299	**£10**	Brown		
		Prefix coding: Letter, number, number.		
		Quantity printed: 40 million.		
		Serial letter:		
		A - - (series traced from A01 to A40)	30	15
B300	**£10**	Brown replacement note		
		Prefix coding: Letter, number, number.		
		Quantity printed: Not known.		
		Serial letter:		
		M - - (series may exist in M01)	—	—

B299

Originally it was thought that the Bank used the M-- star note system for the £10 from the start of Series C, but so far there have been no proven sightings of either Hollom or Fforde notes. B300 may therefore only exist as hand numbered replacements using the A-- prefix.

Collectors should be aware that 01 (or other) first prefixes, linking prefixes and closing prefixes are likely to command a premium in EF grade.

For classification of specimen notes and errors see pages 140–145.

JOHN STANDISH FFORDE (1966–1970)
(The 24th Chief Cashier)

© Bank of England

John Fforde was born on 16 November 1921. He was educated at Rossall School and Christ Church College, Oxford. After serving as a pilot in the R.A.F. during the war he returned to Oxford where he became a Fellow of Nuffield College. He entered Bank service in 1957 and spent four years as Deputy Head of the Central Banking Information Department. In 1964 he became Advisor to the Governor and was appointed Chief Cashier on 1 July 1966 a position he held to 28 February 1970. He was an Executive Director from 1970 to 1982 and was again Advisor to the Governor from 1982–84.

1967 (15 February) ONE POUND

Design, watermark and dimensions as for L. K. O'Brien Portrait Series C notes. Plate-printed at the Bank of England Works, Loughton, Essex. Some notes (B303, B307 and B308) carry a small capital letter 'G' on the reverse indicating that they were printed in sheets of 21 (7 × 3) on an experimental German Goebel press. By 1968 the existing serial letter combinations (B301) had been exhausted so the Bank started to use the first half of the alphabet as the control letter (B305).

			EF	VF
B301	**£1**	Green		
		Prefix coding: Letter, number, number, letter.		
		Quantity printed: 1,475 million.		
		Serial letters:		
		B - - Y (first series traced from B12Y)	25	12
		C - - Y , D - - Y , ** , H - - Y , J - - Y , K - - Y , L - - Y		
		A - - Z , B - - Z , C - - Z , D - - Z , E - - Z , H - - Z , J - - Z , **	4	—
		L - - Z (last series traced to L99Z)	25	10

** For prefix gaps see 'G' notes under B303 below.

FFORDE (contd.)

			EF	VF
B302	**£1**	Green replacement note *Prefix coding:* Letter, number, number, letter (type 1). *Quantity printed:* 38 million. *Serial letters:*		
		M-R (series traced from M09R to M49R)	15	8
B303	**£1**	Green (printed on a Goebel machine) *Prefix coding:* Letter, number, number, letter (type 1). *Quantity printed:* 198 million. *Serial letters ('G' reverse):*		
		E-Y (series traced from E01Y)	5	—
		K-Z (series traced to K81Z)	5	—
B304	**£1**	Green replacement note (printed on a Goebel machine) *Prefix coding:* Letter, number, number, letter (type 1). *Quantity printed:* 14 million. *Serial letters ('G' reverse):*		
		M-N (series traced from M29N to M42N)	35	15
B305	**£1**	Green *Prefix coding:* Letter, number, number, letter (type 2). *Quantity printed:* 4,000 million (estimated). *Serial letters:*		
		N-A (first series traced from N01A)	18	10
		N-B, N-C, N-D, N-E, N-H, N-J, N-K, N-L		
		R-A, ** , R-C, R-D, R-E, R-H, R-J, R-K, **		
		S-A, S-B, S-C, S-D, S-E, S-H, S-J, S-K, S-L	3	—
		T-A, T-B, T-C, T-D, T-E, T-H, T-J, T-K, T-L		
		U-A, U-B, U-C, U-D, ** , U-H		
		W-A, W-B, W-C, **		
		** , X-B		
		X-C (last series traced to X42C)	35	15

    **   For prefix overlaps and gaps see 'G' notes under B307 below and under Page B320.

			EF	VF
B306	**£1**	Green replacement note *Prefix coding:* Letter, number, number, letter (type 2). *Quantity printed:* 300 million. *Serial letters (overlaps with Page):*		
		R-M (series traced between R01M and R53M)	15	5
		S-M (series traced between S01M and S72M)	10	4
		T-M (series traced between T01M and T04M)	125	75
		U-M (series traced in U01M only)	25	10

	EF	VF

B307 **£1**   Green (printed on a Goebel machine)
Prefix coding: Letter, number, number, letter (type 2).
Quantity printed: 250 million.
Serial letters ('G' reverse):

	EF	VF
R - - B (series traced from R01B to R - - B)	5	—
R - - L (series traced from R01L to R99L)	5	—
U - - E (series traced from U01E to U - - E)	5	—

B308 **£1**   Green replacement note (printed on a Goebel machine)
Prefix coding: Letter, number, number, letter (type 2).
Quantity printed: 25 million.
Serial letters ('G' reverse):

	EF	VF
N - - M (series traced from N01M to N14M)	20	10
T - - M (series traced from T29M to T32M)	125	75

£1 notes bearing the signature of J. B. Page were issued concurrently with those of J. S. Fforde for two years with several serial prefixes shared by both cashiers, and overlaps occur. Pairs with consecutive serial numbers from £150 (*EF*).

1967 (15 February) TEN SHILLINGS

Design, watermark and dimensions as for L. K. O'Brien Series C portrait notes. Printed at the Bank of England Works, Loughton, Essex.

B309 **10s.**   Red-brown
Prefix coding: Number, number, letter.
Quantity printed: 768 million.
Serial letters:

	EF	VF
- - R (first series traced from 26R)	15	8
- - S , - - T , - - U, - - W, - - X , - - Y	3	—
- - Z (last series traced to 99Z)	5	—

B310 **10s.**   Red-brown
Prefix coding: Letter, number, number, letter.
Quantity printed: 335 million.
Serial letters:

	EF	VF
A - - N (first series traced from A01N)	6	—
B - - N, C - - N	3	—
D - - N (last series traced to D38N)	5	—

FFORDE (contd.)

			EF	VF
B311	**10s.**	Red-brown replacement note *Prefix coding:* Letter, number, number. *Quantity printed:* 25 million. *Serial letter:*		
		M - - (series traced from M56 to M80)	12	5

1967 (9 January) FIVE POUNDS

Design, watermark and dimensions as for J. Q. Hollom notes. Printed at the Bank of England Works, Loughton, Essex.

B312	**£5**	Blue *Prefix coding:* Letter, number, number. *Quantity printed:* 775 million. *Serial letters:*		
		R - - (first series traced from R20)	45	20
		S - -, T - -, U - -, W - -, X - -, Y - -	15	8
		Z - - (last series traced to Z99)	25	12
B313	**£5**	Blue replacement note *Prefix coding:* Letter, number, number. *Quantity printed:* 30 million. *Serial letters:*		
		M - - (series traced from M08 to M38)	60	35
B314	**£5**	Blue *Prefix coding:* Number, number, letter. *Quantity printed:* 850 million (including B324). *Serial letters (overlap with Page):*		
		- - A (first series traced from 01A)	25	12
		- - B, - - C, - - D, - - E, - - H, - - J , - - K	15	10
		- - L (last series traced to 40L)	45	20
B315	**£5**	Blue replacement note *Prefix coding:* Number, number, letter. *Quantity printed:* 15 million (including B325). *Serial letters (overlap with Page):*		
		- - M (series traced from 01M to 15M)	75	40

£5 notes bearing the signature of J. B. Page were issued concurrently with those of J. S. Fforde with several serial prefixes shared by both cashiers, and overlaps occur. Pairs with consecutive serial numbers from £175 (*EF*).

1967 (9 January) TEN POUNDS

Design, watermark and dimensions as for J. Q. Hollom notes. Printed at the Bank of England Works, Loughton, Essex.

			EF	*VF*
B316	**£10**	Brown		

Prefix coding: Letter, number, number.
Quantity printed: 54 million.
Serial letters:
A-- (series traced from A41 to A95)   30   15

B317 **£10** Brown replacement note
Prefix coding: Letter, number, number.
Quantity printed: Not known.
Serial letters:
M-- (series may exist in M01)   —   —

Originally it was thought that the Bank used the M-- star note system for the £10 from the start of Series C, but so far there have been no proven sightings of either Hollom or Fforde notes. B317 may therefore only exist as hand numbered replacements using the A-- prefix.

£10 notes bearing the signature of J. B. Page were issued concurrently with those of J. S. Fforde and overlaps occur. Pairs with consecutive serial numbers from £200 (*EF*).

Collectors should be aware that 01 (or other) first prefixes, linking prefixes and closing prefixes are likely to command a premium in EF grade.

FFORDE (contd.)

SERIES D (PICTORIAL) 1970–PRESENT

The Pictorial Series D notes, £50, £20, £10 and £5 are the work of Harry Eccleston, assisted by Roger Withington and David Wicks. (The £1 ceased to be legal tender on 11 March 1988). Eccleston joined the Bank in January 1958 and later became the first full time banknote designer. By the time the £50 note was issued in 1981, nearly 20 years work had gone into the series with a great deal of innovation in both design and production. Harry Eccleston himself retired in January 1983 and Roger Withington took over as chief designer.

In fact Eccleston's earliest work on the Series D was for a new 10s. note. As he recalls in an interview for *The Moneymakers International* (op cit) "It was a beautiful note to design—all offset in various shades of brown and orange, with *Sir Walter Raleigh* as the historical figure on the reverse ... but in 1964 when the design was approved and production was just getting underway, the Government decided to bring out the 50 pence coin instead so my first English banknote was stillborn".

1970 (9 July) TWENTY POUNDS

Designed by Harry Eccleston, featuring on the obverse the Queen's portrait with a vignette of St. George and the dragon; the reverse shows the statue of Shakespeare from the Kent Memorial in Westminster Abbey and a scene from *Romeo and Juliet*. Plate-printed in sheets of 15 (5 × 3) at the Bank of England Works, Loughton, Essex, on banknote paper manufactured by Portals Ltd. with watermark of the Queen's head. The notes measure 160mm × 90mm ($6\frac{5}{16} \times 3\frac{9}{16}$ in.) and are still legal tender. Although the first issue was signed by J. S. Fforde, he had ceased to be Chief Cashier four months previously in March 1970.

			EF	VF
B318	**£20**	Multicoloured (purple predominating) *Prefix coding:* Letter, number, number. *Quantity printed:* 5 million. *Serial letter:*		
		A 01 (first series)	95	45
		A - - (series traced to A05)	75	—

			EF	*VF*
B319	**£20**	Multicoloured replacement note		

Prefix coding: Letter, number, number.
Quantity printed: under 1 million.
Serial letter:
    M01 (only)   185   70

For classification of specimen notes and errors see pages 140–145.

© Bank of England

JOHN BRANGWYN PAGE
(1970–1980)
(The 25th Chief Cashier)

John Page was born on 23 August 1923. He was educated at Highgate School and King's College, Cambridge. Having served as a pilot in the R.A.F. during the war he joined the Bank in 1948. He was seconded for two years to the I.M.F. in 1953. He was appointed Assistant Chief Cashier in 1966 and First Deputy Chief Cashier March in 1968. He held the post of Chief Cashier (which he said he enjoyed more than anything else he had ever done) from 1 March 1970 to 29 February 1980 and was subsequently an Executive Director 1980–82.

SERIES C (PORTRAIT)

1971 (date unknown) ONE POUND

Design, watermark and dimensions as for L. K. O'Brien portrait notes. Printed on sheet fed or continuous reel-fed machines at the Bank of England Works, Loughton, Essex.

			EF	VF
B320	**£1**	Green		

Prefix coding: Letter, number, number, letter.
Quantity printed: 3,900 million (estimated).
Serial letters:

	EF	VF
S - - L (first series traced in S87L, S89L, S90L only)	125	50
** , T - - B , ** , T - - D , T - - E , T - - H , ** , T - - K , T - - L		
U - - A , U - - B , U - - C , U - - D , ** , U - - H		
W - - A , W - - B , W - - C , W - - D , W - - E , W - - H	3	—

** For prefix overlaps and gaps see under Fforde B305 and B307.

From here on the sheet size changes to 21 notes and the highest serial prefix becomes 84.

	EF	VF
X - - A , X - - B , X - - C , X - - D , X - - E , X - - H , X - - J , X - - K , X - - L	3	—
Y - - A , Y - - B , Y - - C , Y - - D , Y - - E , Y - - H , Y - - J , Y - - K , Y - - L		
Z - - A , Z - - B , Z - - C , Z - - D , Z - - E , Z - - H , Z - - J , Z - - K		
Z - - L (last series traced to Z84L)	15	5

B321 **£1** Green replacement note
Prefix coding: Letter, number, number, letter.
Quantity printed: 300 million.
Serial letters:

	EF	VF
R - - M (series traced between R44M and R99M)	15	5
S - - M (series traced between S35M and S98M)	10	3

From here on the sheet size changes to 21 notes and the highest serial prefix becomes 84.

	EF	VF
W- - M (series traced between W01M and W84M)	8	3
X - - M (series traced between X01M and X60M)	12	5

£1 notes bearing the signature of J. B. Page were issued concurrently with those of J. B. Fforde for two years with many serial prefixes shared by both cashiers, and overlaps occur. Pairs with consecutive serial numbers from £150 (*EF*).

By mid 1973, the existing serial combinations were almost used up, and the Bank of England introduced the serial prefix letter, letter, number, number for the first time. From 1974 all £1 notes were printed on reel-fed presses in sheets of 21.

B322 **£1** Green
Prefix coding: Letter, letter, number, number.
Quantity printed: 4,715 million.
Serial letters:

	EF	VF
A N - - (first series traced from AN01)	8	—
A R - -, A S - -, A T - -, A U - -, A W - -, A X - -, A Y - -, A Z - -		
B N - -, B R - -, B S - -, B T - -, B U - -, B W - -, B X - -, B Y - -, B Z - -		
C N - -, C R - -, C S - -, C T - -, C U - -, C W - -, C X - -, C Y - -, C Z - -	3	—
D N - -, D R - -, D S - -, D T - -, D U - -, D W - -, D X - -, D Y - -, D Z - -		
E N - -, E R - -, E S - -, E T - -, E U - -, E W - -, E X - -, E Y - -, E Z - -		
H N - -, H R - -, H S - -, H T - -, H U - -, H W - -, H X - -, H Y - -		
H Z - - (last series traced to HZ62)	10	—

PAGE (contd.)

			EF	VF
B323	**£1**	Green replacement note (but not all were used as such)		

Prefix coding: Letter, letter, number, number.
Quantity printed: Fewer than 400 million.
Serial letters:

	EF	VF
MR - - (first series traced from MR01)	10	—
MS - -	7	—
MT - -	7	—
MU - -	7	—
MW - - (last series traced to MW19)	8	—

1971 (date unknown) FIVE POUNDS

Design, watermark and dimensions as for J. Q. Hollom notes. Printed at the Bank of England Works, Loughton, Essex. At some stage (date unknown) the sheet size was changed from 18 to 21 (7 × 3).

B324 **£5** Blue
Prefix coding: Number, number, letter.
Quantity printed: 850 million (including B314)
Serial letters:

	EF	VF
- - C (first series traced from 03C)	30	15
- - F , - - E , - - H , - - J , - - K	20	10
- - L (last series traced to 30L)	35	20

B325 **£5** Blue replacement note
Prefix coding: Number, number, letter.
Quantity printed: 18 million (including B315)
Serial letter:

	EF	VF
- - M (series traced from 04M to 18M)	75	45

£5 notes bearing the signature of J. B. Page were issued concurrently with those of J. S. Fforde. Several serial prefixes were shared by both cashiers and overlaps occur. Pairs with consecutive serial numbers from £175 (*EF*).

1971 (date unknown) TEN POUNDS

Design, watermark and dimensions as for J. Q. Hollom notes. Printed at the Bank of England Works, Loughton, Essex.

B326 **£10** Brown
Prefix coding: Letter, number, number.
Quantity printed: 350 million.
Serial letters:

	EF	VF
A - - (first series traced from A92)	150	75
B - - , C - -	25	15

Originally the series was thought to end in E--, but so far there are no proven sightings of D-- or E-- prefixes.

                                                                  EF   *VF*

B327 **£10**   Brown replacement note
                 Prefix coding: Letter, number, number.
                 Quantity printed: 17 million.
                 Serial letter:
                 M- - (series traced from M01 to M17)   35   16

£10 notes bearing the signature of J. B. Page were issued concurrently with
those of J. S. Fforde and overlaps occur. Pairs with consecutive serial
numbers from £200 (*EF*).

Collectors should be aware that 01 (or other) first prefixes, linking
prefixes and closing prefixes are likely to command a premium in EF grade.

For classification of specimen notes and errors see pages 140–145.

SERIES D (PICTORIAL)

For design details see page 114.

1970 (date unknown) TWENTY POUNDS

Design, dimensions and watermark as for J. S. Fforde notes. Printed at the
Bank of England Works, Loughton.

B328 **£20**   Multicoloured (purple predominating)
                 Prefix coding: Letter, number, number.
                 Quantity printed: 350 million.
                 Serial letters:
                 A- - (first series traced from A06)   60   35
                 B- -, C- -   45   —
                 D- - (last series traced to D79)   50   25

B329 **£20**   Multicoloured replacement note
                 Prefix coding: Letter, number, number.
                 Quantity printed: 2½ million.
                 Serial letter:
                 M- - (series traced from M01 to M04)   75   45

1975 (20 February) TEN POUNDS

Designed by Harry Eccleston as the fourth in the Pictorial Series D notes.
The obverse features the Queen's portrait in State Robes, a medallion of
Britannia and a vignette derived from the lily symbol used by Florence
Nightingale. On the reverse the portrait of Florence Nightingale was
created from photographs taken on her return from the Crimean War. It is
set beside a vignette based on a contemporary lithograph showing her at
work in the Barracks Hospital, Scutari. Plate-printed in sheets of 20 (5 × 4)
at the Bank of England Works, Loughton, Essex, on banknote paper

PAGE (contd.)

manufactured by Portals Ltd., with watermark of Florence Nightingale's head. The notes measure 151mm × 84.87mm ($5\frac{7}{8}$ × $3\frac{5}{16}$in.) and are still legal tender.

			EF	VF
B330	**£10**	Multicoloured (brown predominating)		
		Prefix coding: Letter, number, number.		
		Quantity printed: 1,200 million.		
		Serial letters:		
		A 01 (first series)	60	40
		A - -, B - -, C - -, D - -, E - -, H - -, J - -, K - -, L - -,		
		N - -, R - -, S - -, T - -	25	—
		U - - (last series traced in U39 only)	120	60

There may be an overlap here with Somerset £10 U-- prefix but see comment under B340 regarding replacements.

			EF	VF
B331	**£10**	Multicoloured replacement note		
		Prefix coding: Letter, number, number.		
		Quantity printed: Not known.		
		Serial letters:		
		M - - (series traced from M01 to M50 not inclusive)	60	40

This note may well have been used for general circulation.

1971 (11 November) FIVE POUNDS

Designed by Harry Eccleston as the third in the Pictorial Series D notes. On the obverse it features the Queen's portrait, a medallion of Britannia and a vignette depicting a Winged Victory, a symbol of military prowess. On the reverse there is a portrait of the first Duke of Wellington and a vignette of a scene based on a 19th century engraving of the Battle of Fuentes de Onoro which took place in 1811 during the Peninsular War. Initially plate-printed in sheets of 18 (6 × 3) at the Bank of England Works, Loughton, Essex, on banknote paper manufactured by Portals Ltd., with continuous watermark of Wellington's head. The notes measure 145.5mm × 77.8mm ($5\frac{3}{4}$ × $3\frac{1}{16}$in.) and are still legal tender. From 1973 the notes were printed on the web presses, intaglio on the front and offset litho on the back. The new notes had a small capital 'L' (for Litho) on the back.

		EF	*VF*

B332   **£5**   Multicoloured (pale blue predominating)
Prefix coding: Letter, number, number.
Quantity printed: 810 million.
Serial letters:

	EF	*VF*
A 01 (first series)	40	20
A - -, B - -, C - -, D - -, E - -, H - -, J - -, K - -	18	—
L - - (last series traced to L94)	35	18

B333   **£5**   Multicoloured replacement note
Prefix coding: Letter, number, number.
Quantity printed: 4½ million.
Serial letter:

	EF	*VF*
M - - (series traced from M01 to M05)	65	35

1973 (August) FIVE POUNDS

Design, dimensions and watermark as for B332 above, but printed on web presses in sheets of 18 (6 × 3). The front main design is by intaglio and the back by offset lithography. The notes are distinguished by a small capital letter 'L' on the reverse by the £5 sign at the bottom left corner.

B334   **£5**   Multicoloured (pale blue predominating)
Prefix coding: Number, number, letter.
Quantity printed: 1,600 million.
Serial letters:

	EF	*VF*
01A (first series)	45	25
- - A, - - B, - - C, - - D, - - E, - - H, - - J , - - K, - - L, - - N, - - R, - - S , - - T , - - U, - - W, - - X , - - Y	18	—
- - Z (last series traced to 83Z)	35	18

B335   **£5**   Multicoloured replacement note
Prefix coding: Number, number, letter.
Quantity printed: 8 million.
Serial letter:

	EF	*VF*
- - M (series traced from 01M to 08M)	65	35

B336   **£5**   Multicoloured (pale blue predominating)
Prefix coding: Letter, letter, number, number.
Quantity printed: 2,200 million.
Serial letters:

	EF	*VF*
A N01 (first series)	35	18
A N- -, A R - -, A S - -, A T - -, A U- -, A W- -, A X - -, A Y- -, A Z - - B N- -, B R - -, B S - -, B T - -, B U- -, B W- -, B X - -, B Y- -, B Z - - C N- -, C R - -, C S - -, C T - -, C U- -, C W- -, C X - -	15	—
D series not traced in P age		
E Z - - (last series traced from EZ52 to EZ56)	45	25

It is possible that EZ56 was an experimental note as the prefix is also found in D. H. F. Somerset £5 notes.

PAGE (contd.)

1978 (9 February) ONE POUND

Designed by Harry Eccleston as the fifth in the Pictorial Series D notes. The obverse has the same portrait of the Queen as used on the £5 note, and features a medallion of Britannia, a vignette of a design comprising a caduceus, cornucopia and an olive branch, combined in multicoloured patterns of green, yellow and blue. On the reverse is a portrait in green of Sir Isaac Newton specially created from a number of contemporary portraits, together with multicoloured machine-engraved patterns suggesting the solar system, overlaid by a geometric diagram from Newton's *Principia*.

Plate-printed in sheets of 40 (8 × 5), and later (B340) in sheets of 21 (7 × 3) on continuous reel machines, at the Bank of England Works, Loughton, Essex, on banknote paper manufactured by Portals Ltd., with watermark of Newton's head. A particular feature of the note was that it only had one serial number, printed at the bottom right hand corner. The top left hand side was left blank for encoding marks which could be used by electronic note sorting machines. The notes measure 66.69mm × 134.5mm ($2\frac{5}{8}$ × $5\frac{5}{16}$in.) and ceased to be legal tender on 11 March 1988.

			EF	VF
B337	**£1**	Multicoloured (green predominating)		
		Prefix coding: Letter, number, number.		
		Quantity printed: 1,440 million.		
		Serial letters:		
		A 01 (first series)	6	3
		A--, B--, C--, D--, E--, H--, J--, K--, L,		
		N--, R--, S--, T--, U--, W--, X--, Y--	—	—
		Z-- (last series traced to Z80)	8	4
B338	**£1**	Multicoloured replacement note		
		Prefix coding: Letter, number, number.		
		Quantity printed: Probably 1 million.		
		Serial letter:		
		M01 (only)	85	40

Although these notes were prepared as replacements, there is no evidence that they were used for this purpose since the so-called star note system had been superseded by automatic replacements using Crosfield counting machines and computerised records.

			EF	*VF*

B339 **£1**   Multicoloured (green predominating)
Prefix coding: Number, number, letter.
Quantity printed: 1,360 million.
Serial letters:

	EF	*VF*
01A (first series)	8	4
--A, --B, --C, --D, --E, --H, --J, --K, --L, --N, --R, --S, --T, --U, --X, --Y	—	—
--Z (last series traced in 81Z only)	175	60

It is possible that 81Z is an experimental note since it falls outside the range of 80 serial prefixes normally used for this series.

B340 **£1**   Multicoloured (green predominating)
Prefix coding: Letter, number, number, letter.
Quantity printed: 475 million.
Serial letters:

	EF	*VF*
A 01N (first series)	10	5
A--N, B--N, C--N, D--N	5	—
E--N (last series traced to E84N)	8	4

A single copy of a £1 note with the prefix AN01 in the new colours used for D. H. F. Somerset (B341) has been discovered with the signature of J. B. Page and the number 431011. It is supported each side by Somerset notes AN01 431010 and 431012. The explanation is that this is almost certainly a replacement note. Although the 'star' note system (see page 138) no longer exists hand numbered replacements are occasionally necessary if notes are damaged between the counting and packing stages. In the interests of economy, the Bank does not necessarily destroy good notes from experimental runs, and what seems to have happened is that there must have been a successful experimental run using the new colours during Page's term of office. A few unnumbered sheets were probably set aside and used as replacements without anyone realising the signature had changed in the meantime.

For classification of specimen notes and errors see pages 140–145.

© Bank of England

DAVID HENRY FITZROY SOMERSET (1980–1988)
(The 26th Chief Cashier)

David Somerset was born in 1930. He was educated at Wellington College and Peterhouse, Cambridge. He joined the Bank in 1952 and from 1959–62 was seconded as personal assistant to the Managing Director of the I.M.F. On his return he became private secretary to the Governor, Lord Cromer. Nicknamed 'Boomer', he was appointed Deputy Chief Cashier in 1973 and was promoted to Chief Cashier on 1 March 1980. He remained in office until 28 February 1988, when he retired.

Collectors with previous editions of *English Paper Money* should be aware that the catalogue numbers from here on have been changed to allow for the various new issues.

1981 (20 March) ONE POUND

Design, dimensions and watermark as for J. B. Page Pictorial Series D notes, but the general appearance is enhanced by the inclusion of additional background colours, mainly lilac, light green, pink and yellow. The Queen's portrait is more sharply defined and the portrait of Sir Isaac Newton appears rather more lively. Printed on web presses in sheets of 21 (7 × 3) at the Bank of England Works, Loughton on banknote paper manufactured by Portals Ltd. The main design on the front is printed by intaglio and the back by offset lithography. The new notes used different serial prefixes and had a small capital 'W' on the reverse (standing for 'Web' press).

EF   VF

B341 **£1**   Multicoloured (green predominating).
Prefix coding: Letter, letter, number, number.
Quantity printed:
Serial letters:

A N 01 (first series)   8   —

A N - -, A R - -, A S - -, A T - -, A U - -, A W - -, A X - -, A Y - -, A Z - -

B N - -, B R - -, B S - -, B T - -, B U - -, B W - -, B X - -, B Y - -, B Z - -   4   —

C N - -, C R - -, C S - -, C T - -, C U - -, C W - -, C X - -, C Y - -, C Z - -

D N - -, D R - -, D S - -, D T - -, D U - -, D W - -, D X - -, D Y - -

D Y 21 (last series)*   30   15

*The highest numbered £1 note printed was DY21 999997 and this can be seen in the Bank's museum.

A single copy of a £1 note with the prefix AN01 has been discovered with the signature of J. B. Page and the number 431011. For details see under B340.

B342 **£1**   Multicoloured experimental note.
Prefix coding: Letter, letter, number, number.
Quantity printed:
Serial letter:

MN - - (series traced from MN04 to MN18)   200   100

SOMERSET (contd.)

1980 (June) FIVE POUNDS

Design, dimensions and watermark as for J. B. Page series D (Pictorial) notes. Printed on web presses in sheets of 18 at the Bank of England Works, Loughton, Essex. The notes are distinguished by a small capital letter 'L' on the bottom left of the reverse (standing for Litho).

			EF	VF
B343	**£5**	Multicoloured (pale blue predominating).		
		Prefix coding: Letter, letter, number, number.		
		Quantity printed:		
		Serial letters:		
		D N 01 (first series)	30	—
		D N --, D R --, D S --, D T --, D U --, D W--, D X --, D Y --, D Z --		
		E N --, E R --, E S --, E T --, E U --, E W--, E X --, E Y --, E Z --		
		H N --, H R --, H S --, H T --, H U --, H W--, H X --, H Y --, H Z --		
		J N --, J R --, J S --, J T --, J U --, J W--, J X --, J Y --, J Z --		
		K N --, K R --, K S --, K T --, K U --, K W--, K X --, K Y --, K Z --		
		L N --, L R --, L S --, L T --, L U --, L W--, L X --, L Y --	12	—
		L Z -- (last series traced to LZ89)	20	—

The EZ-- prefix is also found in J. B. Page £5 notes.

Prefix now altered to combine letters from the second half of the alphabet with those of the first half.

			EF	VF
		N A 01 (first series)	18	—
		N A --, N B --	12	—
		N C -- (last series traced to NC90)	16	—
B344	**£5**	Multicoloured experimental notes for Optical Character Recognition (OCR).		
		Prefix coding: Letter, letter, number, number.		
		Quantity printed: Not known.		
		Serial letters:		
		AN91, BR91, CS91, DT91, EU91, HW91, JX91, KY91, LZ91	250	175

Five pound notes are prepared in sheets of 18, so that five sheets used up 90 serial numbers. The serial 91 therefore falls outside the normal range.

For further details of sheet make-up see page 149.

1987 (16 July) FIVE POUNDS

Design, dimensions and watermark as for J. B. Page Pictorial Series D notes. Notes now have a thread 1mm wide as opposed to the 0.5mm thread in previous issues to make it more easily visible. Printed on web presses in sheets of 18 at the Bank of England Works, Loughton, Essex.

		EF	VF
B345 **£5**	Multicoloured		

Prefix coding: Letter, letter, number, number.
Quantity printed:
Serial letters:

	EF	VF
R A 01 (first series)	18	—
R A - -, R B - -	12	—
R C - - (last series traced to RC90)	16	—

1980 (December) TEN POUNDS

Design, dimensions and watermark as for J. B. Page Pictorial Series D notes. Plate-printed in sheets of 20 at the Bank of England Works, Loughton, Essex.

B346 **£10**   Multicoloured (brown predominating).
Prefix coding: Letter, number, number.
Quantity printed:
Serial letters:

	EF	VF
U 01 (first series)	40	—
U - -, W - -, X - -, Y - -	20	—
Z - - (last series traced to Z80)	35	—

SOMERSET (contd.)

			EF	VF
B347	**£10**	Multicoloured (brown predominating).		

Prefix coding: Number, number, letter.
Quantity printed:
Serial letters:

	EF	VF
01A (first series)	35	—
- - A , - - B , - - C , - - D , - - E , - - H , - - J , - - K	20	—
- - L (last series traced to 40L)	35	—

1984 (20 February) TEN POUNDS

Design, dimensions and watermark as for J. B. Page Pictorial Series D notes. Printed on Web presses in sheets of 15 (5 × 3) with the front main design by intaglio and the back by offset lithography. The notes are distinguished by a small capital letter 'L' (standing for Litho) on the bottom left of the reverse.

B348	**£10**	Multicoloured (brown predominating).	

Prefix coding: Letter, letter, number, number.
Quantity printed:
Serial letters:

	EF	VF
A N 01 (first series)	30	—
A N - - , A R - - , A S - - , A T - - , A U - - , A W - - , A X - - , A Y - - , A Z - -		
B N - - , B R - - , B S - - , B T - - , B U - - , B W - - , B X - - , B Y - - , B Z - -		
C N - -	20	—
C R - - (last series traced to CR90)	25	—

1987 (16 July) TEN POUNDS

Design, dimensions and watermark as for J. B. Page Pictorial Series D notes, but now incorporating a 1mm windowed thread similar to that in the £20 note (B351). There are also some minor changes to the background behind the Queen's portrait.

B349

	EF	VF

B349 **£10**   Multicoloured (brown predominating).
Prefix coding: Letter, letter, number, number.
Quantity printed:
Serial letters:

	EF	VF
C S 01 (first series)	25	—
C S --, C T --, C U--, C W--, C X--, C Y--, C Z--	20	—
D N-- (last series traced to DN30)	35	—

1981 (March) TWENTY POUNDS

Design, dimensions and watermark as for J. S. Fforde Pictorial Series D notes. Plate-printed in sheets of 20 at the Bank of England Works, Loughton, Essex.

B350 **£20**   Multicoloured (purple predominating).
Prefix coding: Letter, number, number.
Quantity printed:
Serial letters:

	EF	VF
E 01 (first series)	55	—
E --, H--	40	—
J -- (last series traced to J40)	50	—

1984 (15 November) TWENTY POUNDS

Design and dimensions as for J. S. Fforde Pictorial Series D notes, but now incorporating a new watermark of Shakespeare's head and a windowed or stardust thread which appears as a line of dashes until it is held to the light. There are also some changes in the ink colours with more emphasis on green and brown areas and the note has a more sharply defined appearance. Plate-printed in sheets of 20 at the Bank of England Works, Loughton, Essex.

B351

SOMERSET *(contd.)*

B351 **£20**   Multicoloured
                Prefix coding: Number, number, letter.
                Quantity printed:
                Serial letters:

	EF	VF
01A (first series)	50	—
--A, --B, --C, (--D, --E, --H), --J	40	—
--K (last series traced to 40K)	50	—

1981 (20 March) FIFTY POUNDS

Designed by Harry Eccleston and Roger Withington as the fifth in the Pictorial Series D notes. The obverse has the same portrait of the Queen as used on the £10 and £20 notes, and features a Phoenix based on a design by Sir Christopher Wren and patterns derived from various design features in St. Paul's Cathedral; a medallion of Britannia completes the picture. On the reverse is a new portrait of Sir Christopher Wren specially created from contemporary portraits by J. B. Closterman (1695) and Sir Godfrey Kneller (1711). The background comprises a view of St. Paul's from the River Thames, a floor plan and a decorative guilloche developed from the wood carvings by Grinling Gibbons in the south choir aisle. Printed in sheets of 15 (5 × 3) on banknote paper manufactured by Portals Ltd. with watermark of H.M. The Queen and contoured security thread produced by laser equipment manufactured by the U.K. Atomic Energy Authority. The notes measure 169mm × 95mm ($3\frac{3}{4}$ × $6\frac{5}{8}$in.).

B352 **£50**   Multicoloured.
                Prefix coding: Letter, number, number.
                Quantity printed:
                Serial letters:

A 01 (first series)	120	—
A --		
B -- (last series traced to B90)	80	—

For classification of specimen notes and errors see pages 140–145.

© Bank of England

GEORGE MALCOLM GILL (1988–)
(The 27th Chief Cashier)

Malcolm Gill was born on 23 May 1934. He was educated at Cambridgeshire High School and Sidney Sussex College, Cambridge. After National Service in the R.A.F., he joined the Bank in 1957. He was seconded to the office of the U.K. delegation at the I.M.F. in Washington from 1966–68, seconded to H.M. Treasury from 1977–80 and was private secretary to the Governor, Lord O'Brien, from 1970–72. He became Head of the Foreign Exchange Division in 1982 and Chief Cashier from 1 March 1988.

SERIES D (PICTORIAL)

1988 (1 March) FIVE POUNDS

Design, dimensions and watermark as for J. B. Page Pictorial Series D notes, but incorporating 1mm security thread as in D. H. F. Somerset £5 notes (B345). Printed on web presses in sheets of 18 at the Bank of England Works, Loughton, Essex.

			EF	*VF*
B353	**£5**	Multicoloured (blue predominating).		
		Prefix coding: Letter, letter, number, number.		
		Quantity printed:		
		Serial letters:		
		R D 01 (first series)	18	—
		R D --, R E --, R H --, R J --, R K --, R L --		
		S A --, S B --, S C --, S D --, S E --	—	—
		S E 90 (last series)	20	—

GILL (contd.)

1988 (1 March) TEN POUNDS

Design, dimensions and watermark as for J. B. Page Pictorial Series D notes, but incorporating a windowed security thread as in D. H. F. Somerset £10 notes (B349). Printed on web presses in sheets of 15 at the Bank of England Works, Loughton, Essex.

			EF	*VF*
B354	**£10**	Multicoloured (brown predominating).		
		Prefix coding: Letter, letter, number, number.		
		Quantity printed:		
		Serial letters:		
		D R 01 (first series)	25	—
		D R - -, D S - -, D T - -, D U - -, D W- -, D X - -, D Y - -, D Z - -		
		E N - -, E R - -, E S - -, E T - -, E U - -, E W- - (continuing)	—	—

1988 (1 March) TWENTY POUNDS

Design and dimensions as for J. B. Fforde Pictorial Series D notes but incorporating Shakespeare watermark and a windowed security thread as in D. H. F. Somerset £20 notes (B351). Plate printed in sheets of 20 at the Bank of England Works, Loughton, Essex.

B355	**£20**	Multicoloured.		
		Prefix coding: Number, number, letter.		
		Quantity printed:		
		Serial letters:		
		01L (first series)	50	—
		- - L , - - M, - - N, - - R (continuing)	—	—

1988 (21 July) FIFTY POUNDS

Design, dimensions and watermark as for D. H. F. Somerset Pictorial Series D notes, but incorporating a windowed security thread (also known as "Stardust"). The notes also include new colours, in particular a light olive green in the text, the Britannia symbol and the denomination numerals. Plate-printed in sheets of 15 at the Bank of England Works, Loughton, Essex.

B356	**£50**	Multicoloured.		
		Prefix coding: Letter, number, number.		
		Quantity printed:		
		Serial letters:		
		C 01 (first series)	—	—
		C - -, D - - (continuing)		

For classification of specimen notes and errors see pages 140–145.

SERIES E

In October 1988 the Bank of England announced that a new series of English notes, designed by Roger Withington would be introduced in stages from 1990, starting with the £5. The notes, which continued to feature historical figures on the back, also included a new portrait of H.M. The Queen more in keeping with her age, engraved by Alan Dow. The notes differ from previous issues in various respects and incorporate the latest security devices, including a windowed thread and a redesigned watermark. They also have different sized numbers, a coloured denomination symbol to aid the partially-sighted and the international copyright symbol of the Bank of England on the front and the back. When the £5 was issued the Bank announced the historical figures for the other three notes in the series and said that there would also be a different Britannia on each of them.

1990 (7 June) FIVE POUNDS

Designed by Roger Withington, featuring on the obverse the Queen's portrait with a vignette of Britannia and round denomination symbol; the reverse shows a portrait of George Stephenson and early railway history with which he was associated, including the Rocket built by his son, Robert, and Skerne Bridge on the Stockton and Darlington Railway of which he was the engineer. Printed by intaglio in sheets of 18 (6 × 3) at the Bank of England Works, Loughton, Essex, on banknote paper manufactured by Portals with watermark of the Queen's head in registration. The notes measure 70mm × 135mm ($3\frac{5}{8}$ × $5\frac{3}{16}$in.) and are still legal tender.

			EF	VF
B357 **£5**	Multicoloured (turquoise predominating).			
	Prefix coding: Letter, number, number.			
	Quantity printed:			
	Serial letters:			
	A 01 (first series)		—	—
	A - -, B - -, C - -, D - -, (continuing)		—	—

GILL *(contd.)*

1992 (date to be announced) TEN POUNDS

Designed by Roger Withington, featuring on the obverse the Queen's portrait with a vignette of Britannia; the reverse will show a portrait of Michael Faraday and his work on electricity and magnetism. The notes will measure 75mm × 142mm.

EF   VF

B358 **£10**   Multicoloured.
                Prefix coding:
                Quantity printed:
                Serial letters:

1991 (date to be announced) TWENTY POUNDS

Designed by Roger Withington, featuring on the obverse the Queen's portrait with a vignette of Britannia; the reverse will show a portrait of Charles Dickens and scenes from his novels, including Pickwick's village green. The notes will measure 80mm × 149mm.

B359 **£20**   Multicoloured.
                Prefix coding:
                Quantity printed:
                Serial letters:

1994 (date to be announced) FIFTY POUNDS

Designed by Roger Withington, featuring on the obverse the Queen's portrait with a vignette of Britannia; the reverse will show a portrait of Sir John Houblon, first Governor of the Bank of England. The notes will measure 85mm × 156mm.

B360 **£50**   Multicoloured.
                Prefix coding:
                Quantity printed:
                Serial letters:

General Information

General Information

FORMING A COLLECTION

New collectors should aim to keep things as simple as possible to start with. So the first step is to obtain one example of each note to illustrate differences in size, type and colour. This will include one white £5 note, any 10s. and £1 notes from the Series A (Britannia); one of the popular Series B (Helmeted Britannia); one each of the £5 Series C (Portrait), £5 Series D (Pictorial) and £5 Series E; a Portrait 10s. and £1; and a Pictorial £1 note (nicknamed the 'luncheon voucher'). If you can afford it add examples of the Portrait £10 and Pictorial £10, £20 and £50; and one or two of the cheaper Treasury notes. This is called *Type Collecting*.

By this stage you will be aware of the various different Chief Cashiers' signatures on the notes which will whet your appetite for those signatures you do not have. Some are harder to find than others and so at first it is probably advisable to stick to what are termed *middle series* notes. You now have a *Signature Collection*. Add in a few of the commoner *replacement notes* and your collection is acquiring balance.

You will soon realise that the first and last of any series commands a higher price. Like any first edition these are the most desirable notes in any run. The 01 prefixes, the prefixes linking one Chief Cashier to the next, and the last recorded prefixes are elusive and you will need patience and luck to get them. So you may have to be content with any number within the first and last prefixes. You may want an A01 and Z99, but will have to settle for perhaps an A03 and a Z74 because they are available.

Some collectors specialise in all prefixes, that is to obtain an example of every *prefix* in the English series. A more economical method is to go for the first and last in a sub series. An example of this would be under Beale £1 B268. The first of the series is H--B and the last is L--J, but in between there are sub series Z--B, A--C, Z--C, A--J to look for.

Collectors should always aim to acquire notes in the best possible condition. For notes after 1928 this means uncirculated, although it may be virtually impossible with some prefixes. A grading guide will be found on page 152. As far as the earlier notes (and especially those pre-1900) are concerned the best course of action is to buy what is available at whatever price you can afford. Most collectors will be happy with a single example of each of the early cashiers from Newland to Bowen—it gets progressively harder after acquiring a Hase £1. Condition takes second place to actually tracking down the notes since hardly any of the higher denominations are in private hands.

From J. G. Nairne onwards the choice becomes much wider and the Nairne hoard sold by A. F. Brock and Co. at auction on 14 September 1989 added 136 pre-First World War notes to the available supply (12 were retained by the vendor). Treasury notes have become progressively more expensive in recent years especially in uncirculated condition and lesser grades of some varieties are very hard to come by.

When notes are creased or dirty there is a temptation to smarten them up. Some surface marks can be safely removed with a soft india rubber and pressing a note between the pages of a heavy book does no harm. But beware "laundry" jobs.

At best this removes the original sheen; at worst it gives the note a washed out look which destroys its value to collectors. If in doubt, ask the dealer for a written receipt with a guarantee that the note has not been tampered with.

Do not economise on storing your collection. Uncirculated notes in particular must be handled with great care and certain types of vinyl pocket can do irreparable damage by causing notes to sweat or buckle. Advances in technology mean that products are constantly changing, so ask for advice from your dealer and do not begrudge the cost. Make sure you have clean hands and preferably use stamp tweezers when inserting or removing notes from an album.

SERIAL LETTERS AND NUMBERS

Treasury notes are found with serial letters from the whole of the alphabet with the exception of I and Q. The Bank of England has made a rather more selective use of the alphabet which varied over the years. From 1928 the 10s. and £1 notes of C. P. Mahon and B. G. Catterns use all the letters except I, P and Q (which is used for some specimens, see page 140). Later the letters F, G and V were also omitted giving a conveniently round figure of 20 letters available for each issue. The old white notes are found with every serial prefix except F, G and Q. When the Series C (Portrait) notes were introduced in 1960, the letter O letter was dropped and M was adopted for replacements.

The quantity of notes printed in any given issue has been calculated on the basis of one million for each of the serial prefixes 1–99 (100,000 for the white notes). However, it is by no means certain that any given run was completed or if it was put into circulation; the only deciding factor is visual evidence.

One confusing aspect of numbering on the web presses is that it goes backwards from 999999 to 000001. This means that the sheets end up in the right order when they go for guillotining and packing, but does raise the question of precisely which notes are the first and last!

During the Page and Fforde eras there are many overlaps in certain prefixes. One run of 20 £1 notes formerly in the author's collection had no fewer than five changes of signature. The reason for this was that sheet fed notes are printed in several stages and the sheets have to be stored in between. Numbering is the last process and no-one was concerned about the order the stored sheets were used. This cannot happen with the reel-fed presses which carry out the whole printing operation in one go.

REPLACEMENT NOTES

Opinion is divided as to the existence of a recognisable replacement system for Treasury notes. The most tenable theory on the Bradbury first issue is that the notes with double letter prefixes and four numbers were used as replacements. This seems doubtful in view of the speed with which they were produced and similar notes are not found in later issues. From the third issue the odd letter out is Z, which was used as the prefix for the bottom right-hand note of each sheet of £1 notes (though not the 10s.). Numerically these Z notes are relatively scarce, but the author prefers to regard them as control notes rather than replacements.

Bank of England replacement notes (or star notes as they were officially called) were used by the Bank to make up a bundle where one or more notes had been damaged or misprinted. Originally replacement notes were probably set by hand and carried exactly the same serial number as the notes they replaced. This makes them extremely difficult to detect in the unthreaded pre-war issues. Later the Bank adopted a special series of prefixes so that it was easier for them to keep track of the percentage of errors. The numbers of these replacement notes do not fit into the sequence that they are replacing. So, for example, you could be looking at a run from A55 834567 to A55 834573 in which two notes in the middle were replacements carrying the numbers M01 232889 and M01 232890.

Starting with Peppiatt, the serial letter --A was adopted for 10s. replacements and the serial letters S--S and S--T for £1 replacements. Portrait Series C and Pictorial Series D notes use various combinations of the letter 'M'. This does not, however, guarantee that the note is a replacement unless it can be shown as part of a run with ordinary notes because it is known that in later years blocks of 'M' notes were released as the need arose, especially when the system was being phased out.

The star notes were finally discontinued in 1981 soon after the Bank had installed high speed Crosfield counting machines. These are programmed to eliminate notes which the examiners have marked with a yellow felt pen and to make up bundles of the required quantity. At the same time all the serial numbers are stored on computer and print spoils are not substituted so these notes are never issued. It is possible, though unusual for damage to occur or mistakes to be spotted (e.g. a fold in the paper) after the notes have been bundled and in this instance the faulty notes are renumbered and replaced by hand. These are almost impossible to identify though a notable exception was the use of a Page £1 note as a replacement in the first run of Somerset £1 notes AN01 (see under B340).

For convenience the replacement serials are shown here as a group. Detailed tables showing how they fit into the series as a whole are in Appendix A.

Britannia replacement serials

Cashier	10s.	£1
K. O. Peppiatt	01A to 03A	S01S to S09S
P. S. Beale	04A to 35A	S10S to S70S
L. K. O'Brien	36A to 68A	S71S to S97S S01T to S21T

Portrait replacement serials

Cashier	10s.	£1	£1(G)	£5	£10
L. K. O'Brien	M01 to M18	M01 to M68			
J. Q. Hollom	M19 to M55	M68 to M99 01M to 99M M01R to M08R	M01N to M28N	M01 to M07	M01(?)
J. S. Fforde	M56 to M80	M09R to M49R R01M to R53M S01M to S72M T01M to T04M U01M (only)	M29N to M42N N01M to N14M T29M to T32M	M08 to M38 01M to 15M	M01(?)
J. B. Page		R44M to R99M S52M to S98M W01M to W84M X01M to X60M W01M to W81M MR01 to MR48 MS01 to MS84 MT01 to MT21 MU01 to MU18 MW01 to MW19		04M to 18M	M01 to M17

Pictorial replacement serials

Cashier	£1	£5	£5(L)	£10	£20
J. S. Fforde					M01
J. B. Page	M01	M01 to M05	01M to 08M	M01 to M50	M01 to M04
D. H. F. Somerset	MN06/MN18				

TRY FINDING THESE FUN NOTES

COIN	OIL	H20
JOIN	007	M15
LOIN	01C	11N, 21N, etc.
LION	DOI	10Z, 20Z, etc.
BOIL	N01	11B, 21B, etc.
COIL	IOU	10S
SOIL	T42	ER02
TOIL	24T	DIOR

The first printing of the Gill £20 (see B355) is an OIL note!

SPECIMEN NOTES

Specimen notes are issued by the Bank of England to other central banks, but over the years revolutions and the less meticulous attitude to currency in some parts of the world have led to quite a number getting into private hands.

They are nonetheless far scarcer than specimen stamps and few sets have come on to the market in the past 20 years. The earliest white £5 specimen carries the signature of E. M. Harvey and the date 7 September 1922. The Prefix is 001/Q 00000.

Q is also the prefix used for K. O. Peppiatt specimens, or at least for the high denomination notes—a complete set of which was dated 20 April 1934 and was sold at auction by Sotheby's in June 1977.

A set of Second World War notes and post-war Peppiatt specimens came up at a Stanley Gibbons auction in March 1981. The 10s. had the prefix Z00D and the £1 A00D, the same as the issued notes, while the post-war varieties used R00. The £5 white notes were prefixed E00 and L00 respectively, carrying the dates 5 December 1944 and 24 January 1947.

Specimen notes from the Series D and Series E are normally used for publicity purposes by the Bank of England and from photographs that appear in the press we know that the serial numbers are A00 000000.

ERROR NOTES

Considering the millions of notes that are in circulation errors are not common. But collector interest means that examples of faulty printing and paper cutting in modern issues are often spotted by the general public, so there is generally a plentiful supply and prices have never approached the levels of the stamp market.

It is very difficult to classify errors except in broad terms. Treasury errors are rare and the full range is unlikely to be found prior to the Bank of England's Portrait Series C issues. When reel-fed printing started in the Ffforde and Page eras, the incidence is much higher and one wonders how some of them passed the stringent checking process at the Loughton Printing Works.

The answer seems to be that the checkers are geared up to spot minor imperfections; they work at great speed and sometimes real howlers get by. One of the most remarkable errors was the omission of the Chief Cashier's signature in 1981.

A run of D. H. F. Somerset £5 with the serial prefixes DU55 to DU77 escaped, a possible total of 500 sheets or 9,000 notes. The actual range of numbers (last three digits) recorded is between 295 and 532, in other words 237 sheets. This would indicate at least 4,000 were released though some packets were undoubtedly intercepted by the clearing banks and sent back. What would have been a famous error had it been released occurred in the Series E (Stephenson) £5. After the first print run had started in November 1989 it was noticed that Stephenson's date of death had been given as 1845 instead of 1848. About five million of the notes had been produced and these were destroyed. It is not known whether any examples were retained.

The commonest errors are those which involve the corner of a sheet being folded over. A small section of the design then gets printed on the wrong side, and when opened out after guillotining shows a blank area. Other errors fall into two main categories, faulty printing and faulty numbers, and although the main variants are included, the list does not pretend to be exhaustive:

A. Extra paper through faulty folding (generally the sheet corner).
B. Double or faulty printing (e.g. part of the back of the design printed on the front and vice versa).
C. Part of design omitted.
D. Note printed on one side only.
E. Serial numbers missing top and bottom.
F. One serial number missing (or partly missing).
G. Top serial number different from bottom one.
H. Identical serial numbers on a pair (or longer run) of notes.
J. Identical but different serial numbers top and bottom on a pair of notes (slip 'n' stick).
K. Signature omitted.

Ffforde and Page Series C notes are found with each cashier's signature on consecutively numbered pairs (and sometimes longer runs). This is probably due to stacking of the sheets and then mixing them up prior to

Bank of England errors

numbering. They are not errors and will be found listed under the appropriate issue.

It is also worth looking for *correction of error* notes. These occur where a serial number was missing and was later added by hand. Pre-war Bank of England replacement notes may also be identifiable by hand set serials.

PAPER AND PRODUCTION

The first Bank of England notes were written by hand on ordinary paper purchased from stationers. Forgeries led the Bank at a very early stage to experiment with marbled paper which could be matched exactly to a counterfoil. From 1697 watermarked paper was introduced with a watermark of looped border and scroll on the left and the words "Bank of England" at the bottom. It was produced by a Berkshire papermaker, Rice Watkins.

On 27 September 1724 the Bank signed a contract with Henry Portal of Whitchurch, in Hampshire whose firm became the sole papermaker and remains so to this day. No one else is allowed to use the special Bank of England watermarked paper, although Portals themselves are suppliers to well over 100 countries for security printing. The Bank held a stake of 25.5% in the company until 1989 when it was sold on the grounds that a substantial holding in a diversified public company was incompatible with its role as a central bank. The Bank gave an assurance that its relationship as a customer would not be affected by the sale.

For nearly 100 years printing was in the hands of an outside contractor, James Cole until 1748, and then George Cole until 1791. Each month a supply of paper was sent in large iron-bound chests by wagon to the printers in Great Kirby Street, Hatton Garden. Each morning the engraved copper plates would be drawn from the Bank in Threadneedle Street and taken to the printing works where a clerk counted the sheets of notes as they came off the press.

In 1791 Cole's business was transferred to the Bank and from then until 1920 all Bank of England notes were printed on the premises. Despite the decision by Lloyd George to have currency notes issued by the Treasury during the First World War, the Bank's facilities were considerably stretched in printing high denomination notes, postal orders (which were legal tender for a few weeks in 1914), dividend warrants, military allowance drafts, loan issues, Treasury bills, corporation bills and premium exchequer bonds—well over 500 million documents requiring watermarked paper.

The pressure on space at Threadneedle Street was such that in 1916 the Bank purchased St. Luke's Hospital for conversion into a new printing works. Some printing was transferred immediately, but reconstruction did not begin until 1919 and the move was finally completed in April 1922. Thereafter, with the exception of the Second World War emergency issue, all notes were printed at St. Luke's until 1956.

It had become clear some years earlier that a specially designed new printing works would be necessary and accordingly in 1951 the Bank purchased a site at Loughton, in Essex. The new works, occupying half a million square feet of floor space, now employs 1,236 people (as of September 1989) of which about 250 are directly involved in note printing. The main printing hall itself stretches some 300 yards. Additional premises were added later for the destruction of notes which had been withdrawn from circulation.

In 1800 a mere 15,000 notes were printed annually; by 1950 there were 939 million; by 1960 this figure had jumped to 1,627 million and by 1965 to a peak of 2,222 million. Mainly due to the increasing demand in high denomination notes (and the phasing out of the £1) the note issue has fallen. In 1989–90 it was running at around 1,250–1,300 million and allowing for the new Series E production it is expected to be about 1,400 million in 1990–91.

Number of new notes issued by denomination (millions)

Year to end February	1981	1982	1983	1984	1985	1986	1987	1988	1989	1990
£1	893	780	728	652	678	—	—	—	—	—
£5	661	644	622	625	515	522	457	559	475	424
£10	247	219	230	451	456	526	469	515	621	627
£20	44	39	34	72	86	122	78	113	165	194
£50			6	9	9	10	17	18	21	23	22
	1845	1688	1623	1809	1745	1187	1022	1098	1284	1267

Source: *Bank of England Report and Accounts 1980–1990*

More than five million Bank of England notes are printed every working day at Loughton and there are currently about 1,400 million notes in circulation to a total value of more than £13 billion. It will be seen how the usage of the £10 and £20 notes has increased while the £5 is in steady decline, both in terms of the numbers printed and the value in circulation. At the end of the 1970s the £5 accounted for 43% of value; now it is a mere 10%. This trend was clear even before the £1 note was phased out and the relentless march of inflation has also meant people take less care of the £5 so its average life has fallen to between eight and nine months, while the £10 lasts for about 16 months, the £20 for 17 months and the £50 for 23 months.

In a parliamentary answer on 28 February 1989, Lord Young, then Secretary of State for Trade and Industry, said: "In the year to 28 February 1989 the direct cost of paper and other materials used in the production of Bank of England notes was £8.6 million. The total cost of note production was £33 million, and the average cost of each banknote just under 3p. £5 notes cost a little less than the average and £20 and £50 notes cost somewhat more.

Value of notes in circulation by denomination (£ millions)

Year to end February	1981	1982	1983	1984	1985	1986	1987	1988	1989	1990
£1	673	657	641	583	528	142	117	108	102	62
£5	3343	3097	2850	2554	2426	2225	2029	1896	1646	1539
£10	4043	4298	4531	4846	5232	5459	5633	5810	5806	5866
£20	1686	1833	1874	1979	2137	2310	2608	2932	3654	4380
£50	—	274	633	909	1089	1233	1475	1755	2054	2292

Source: *Bank of England Report and Accounts 1980–1990*

To view the trends in a different way the actual number of notes in circulation (millions) looks like this:

Year to end February	1981	1982	1983	1984	1985	1986	1987	1988	1989	1990
£1	673	657	641	583	528	142	117	108	102	62
£5	669	619	570	511	485	445	406	379	329	308
£10	404	430	453	485	523	546	563	581	581	587
£20	84	92	94	99	107	116	130	147	183	219
£50	—	5.5	13	18	22	25	30	35	41	46

Although notes may cease to be legal tender, the Bank's "Promise to Pay the Bearer" is unlimited in time and old notes can always be exchanged for new ones. Remember to check for collector interest first. There is often misunderstanding when a note is withdrawn and when it ceases to be legal tender. Withdrawing a note means that the Bank of England will no longer print and distribute them and as those in circulation are sent back for destruction the issue will gradually disappear. Withdrawing legal tender status happens later; in the case of the Series D Pictorial £1 three years elapsed.

But as the Bank pointed out at the time: "The concept of legal tender is a very narrow one. It is a technical legal term. To tender the correct sum in notes or coin which have the status of 'legal tender' provides a good defence to a charge of non-performance of a contract. The vast majority of people accept notes and coin in financial transactions purely because it is a convenient and accepted way of doing business. The withdrawal of legal tender status makes people less willing to accept the notes, even though they remain payable at the Bank". Put another way shopkeepers may accept notes, but they are not bound to do so.

One important misconception is the status of Scottish and Northern Ireland notes which are not legal tender anywhere in the U.K. and it is entirely up to the recipient as to whether they are acceptable or not. The only people bound to accept them are the issuing banks, which must hold a corresponding number of Bank of England notes in their vaults as collateral.

Most of the work connected with banknote issue is now automated and a record of the serial numbers of all notes printed is kept on computer. Until 1928 registers were kept not only of how many notes were outstanding but which actual notes they were. These registers are still kept for the old white notes of £10 and higher denominations, which means that the bank, given certain guarantees, can replace lost, stolen or badly mutilated notes.

Nowadays the Bank has a department to deal with mutilated notes at its Newcastle branch, set up in 1975, which currently handles more than 27,000 applications a year to a value of about £800,000. Unlike many other countries which pay according to the proportion of the note which survives, the Bank of England either pays out in full or not at all. The section is staffed by six ladies whose ability to reconstruct apparently hopeless cases is remarkable and their work has included damaged notes from the Zeebrugge and Lockerbie disasters, as well as the effects of washing machines, microwave ovens and pets. A fuller description of the department's work will be found in the *Bank of England Quarterly Bulletin* for August 1989.

PRINTING

Until 1960 all notes were printed on sheet-fed presses by the intaglio (recess or line-engraved) process. Sheets of paper were fed singly into the machines which then printed a number of notes from the plate—24 in the case of the Series C (Portrait) £1. The sheets were then stacked and stored so that the ink could dry before the next stage of printing was undertaken. Several printing processes were needed, and the whole operation took several weeks before the notes could be finally sorted, counted and packed. It is still used for £50 notes.

In the late 1950s, however, the Bank assembled a team of engineers to develop a machine that would print the notes in a single process from a reel (or web) of paper into sheets of finished notes. The prototype machine (using components from several different companies) was built by Masson, Scott Thrissell Engineering Ltd., of Bristol, and the first notes, the so-called 'ʀ' £1 notes (B283), appeared in 1960 with the signature of L. K. O'Brien.

In 1962 another web press built by the West German company, Goebel Darmstad, was installed and Hollom and Fforde notes from this machine can be identified by a small capital 'ɢ' appearing on the back. A few years later the Bank opted for Masson, Scott Thrissell machines, six of which were installed by the mid seventies.

Since then the production of all notes (except for the £20 and £50) have been systematically transferred, a process which is marked by a small capital letter 'ʟ' (for Litho) on the back of the notes. There are nine further sheet-fed presses manufactured by De La Rue Giori—three Simultans, one Super Simultan 212, three Intagliocolor 8's, one Super Intagliocolor 212 and one Supernumerota II.

The reels of paper used on the web presses are two miles long and this has meant that they have to be particularly durable, and the watermark can no longer be matched exactly to each note. The £5 web machines produce an average of 1.62 million notes and the £10 webs an average of 1.275 million per 14 hour day divided into two shifts, and in 1989 daily output averaged 5.36 million notes. The Bank is at present working on a new web press which is expected to come on line in about three years. The £20 and £50 notes will, however, continue to be printed on sheet-fed presses.

It is important to understand that the Bank is concerned with the most efficient and economical production of notes consistent with quality and security. What causes excitement among collectors is often just part of a day's work in the eyes of the Bank.

The finished parcels of notes are despatched to the Issue Office of the Bank in London or to one of the five branches, Birmingham, Bristol, Leeds, Manchester and Newcastle where they are held until required by the clearing banks.

The Bank has kindly supplied the following general information on the Series D notes:

Denomination	Sheet size (mm)	Note size (mm)	Notes per sheet	Notes per ream
£5	460.5 × 493.4	145.5 × 77.8	18	9,000
£10	476 × 491.5	151 × 84.87	15	7,500
£20	657 × 495	160 × 90	20	10,000
£50	524 × 518	169 × 95	15	7,500

Denomination	Notes per packet	Packets per bundle	Bundles per parcel	Notes per parcel	Value
£5	100	5	10	5,000	£25,000
£10	100	5	10	5,000	£50,000
£20	50	5	4	1,000	£20,000
£50	50	5	4	1,000	£50,000

It will be seen from the above information that the numbering limits are: £5—90; £10—90; £20—80 and £50—90. Each serial prefix consists of 999,999. Note number 1,000,000 used to be done by hand but these are no longer issued.

DESIGN

For obvious reasons the main consideration in designing a banknote is security against the forger. Although the design of the Bank of England white notes remained largely unchanged for some 250 years there was a great deal of unobtrusive innovation. The vignette of Britannia was changed at fairly regular intervals, until the definitive version was produced by Daniel Maclise, R.A. for the issue of 1855.

The over-riding concern at all times was to keep one jump ahead of the forgers, and to this end the Bank had a constant stream of designs and suggestions. The Bank Restriction period from 1797 was particularly critical and for most of the time a special standing committee was in being to discuss any suitable project.

The best known work was done by Applegarth and Cowper. In December 1817 the Bank's attention was drawn to the work of a printer from Croydon called Augustus Applegarth. He and his partner Edward Cowper were working on surface printing in several colours from blocks to be produced by stereotype from an original cut in wood or metal.

The Committee advanced the sum of £1,200 to develop the system, followed by a further payment of £5,000. In February 1819 after receiving several specimens, the Bank's Court of Directors approved one of the Applegarth and Cowper designs. The plan was to introduce the notes in 1820 and an Act of Parliament was passed to make it illegal to copy the note.

It was described thus: "The groundwork of each banknote will be black or coloured, or black or coloured line work, and the words 'Bank of England' will be replaced at the top of each banknote in white letters upon a black, sable or dark ground, such ground containing white lines intersecting each other, and the numerical amount or sum of each banknote in the body of the note will be printed in black and red register work, and the back of each note will distinctly show the whole contents thereof except the number and date in reversed impression".

By autumn 1821 the Bank had spent a total of £40,000 on developing the new notes only to find that its own engravers were able to imitate every aspect of the Applegarth and Cowper designs. The experiment came to an abrupt end. The full story of this and other schemes can be found in *As Good As Gold* by Virginia Hewitt and John Keyworth (op. cit.).

In 1836 the Bank decided to adopt a new system of printing and engraving then in use in Ireland, which was the invention of John Oldham, who was appointed Mechanical Engineer and Principal of the Engraving, Plate Printing, Numbering and Dating Office. This was in use by 1838 and a committee again started to consider changes in design.

An elaborate new design was recommended "containing allegorical figures representing Britannia standing on a rock with the shield of the union, the armed prow of a ship and the waves beating at her feet . . . in the centre of the bottom is a medallion containing the heads of King William and Queen Mary as founders of the Bank in 1694" (illustrated in *As Good As Gold* page 110). This note, however, was not approved by the Court of Directors and together with other similar allegorical efforts during the first half of the 19th century, can only be classified as an unadopted essay.

The expansion of international trade in the 19th century put great pressure on the currency, dependent as it was on gold for sums below five pounds. An article by Alistair Gibb (*Bond and Banknote News*) gives details of a campaign started in the 1880s by Randolph Churchill, the Chancellor of the Exchequer, to reintroduce the £1 note. The idea was pursued by his successor George Joachim Goschen, who had been a Director of the Bank of England at the age of 27 and who planned to double the supply of money by the issue of notes and the use of securities rather than gold as partial backing. The proposal produced a heated debate and was taken sufficiently seriously by the Bank of England for it to produce a trial £1 note, referred to as the Goschen pound. An illustration of the note, which is in the Bank's archives, accompanies Alistair Gibb's article. It was hardly an inspired design and certainly has none of the elegance of the 1914 pound note with its promise to "pay the bearer in standard gold coin".

Design work on present day notes is a long and painstaking process. Mr. Harry Eccleston, the Bank's Chief Designer from 1962 until January 1983 spent the best part of his career working on the D series notes. In an interview for *The Moneymakers* (op. cit.) he commented: "The canvas is ridiculously tiny and there is no normal 'frame' to your picture—the edge is more of a wavy line. Add to that all the words you are obliged to include for statutory purposes, and then the restrictions that printing from an engraved plate impose upon the monarch's portrait . . . (features) that make the forger's job more difficult, things like micro-lettering, machine engraving and hand engraving, close registered backgrounds, 'white line' and 'black line' vignettes, asymmetrically based patterns, to name but a few. On top of all that, the design has to be capable of mass production on high speed presses so that notes printed years apart look identical when placed side by side".

In 1985 the Bank introduced a computer to help with design. The software package enables complex designs and patterns to be stored and reproduced on a high resolution screen. The new Series E notes which are being designed by Roger Withington (who succeeded Harry Eccleston as Chief Designer in 1983), rely heavily on the CAD system (computer-aided design) as it is called. Advances in technology are such that the Bank is likely to have to change design features more frequently in future to keep ahead of the counterfeiters and to keep up with the needs of Automated Teller Machines (ATMs) and other machines in which notes need to be read and verified. It is unlikely that Series E will last much beyond the year 2,000.

FORGERIES AND 'SKIT' NOTES

Over the years many imitations of Bank of England notes have been produced. Some have been merely frivolous, others have had serious intent, such as George Cruickshank's anti-hanging note aimed at ending the death penalty for passing forged notes. Forgery became a serious problem in the early 19th century during the Bank Restriction period. Some 618 people were sentenced to death for forgery between 1797 and 1829, and it was not until 1832 that the death sentence was finally abolished and transportation for life was substituted.

Today it is an offence for anyone knowingly to purchase, receive from any person, or have in his custody or possession a forged banknote regardless of its age or country of origin. Collectors should familiarise themselves with the provisions of the *Forgery and Counterfeiting Act 1981* (which superseded the *Forgery Act 1913*). This states, *inter alia*, that "it is an offence for any person, unless the relevant authority has previously consented in writing, to reproduce on any substance whatsoever, and whether or not on the correct scale, any British currency note or any part of a British currency note". This clearly covers both photographing and photocopying notes.

In July 1989 the Bank issued "Guidelines for reproducing Bank of England notes in advertisements and illustrations". One important concession regarding old notes (i.e. notes issued before 1960 which do not contain a portrait of the Queen) is that they no longer need to be overprinted "Specimen". Anyone, however, contemplating the reproduction of any Bank of England note of any period is most strongly advised to obtain the guidelines and if in doubt to consult the Bank first.

Forged notes are immediately confiscated by the Bank of England if presented for verification and this still applies to the Second World War forgeries produced by the Nazis at the Sachsenhausen concentration camp. The story of "Operation Andrew" and "Operation Bernhard" is fully chronicled by Bryan Burke in "Nazi Counterfeiting of British Currency during World War II" (see Bibliography).

If the Bank of England establishes that a note is a forgery, it will be confiscated, so collectors are in a cleft stick. Keeping the note, knowing it to be forged, is an offence. By checking it with the Bank, you risk losing it.

DATES

No modern Bank of England notes are dated. Until the introduction of the 10s. and £1 notes in 1928, all denominations carried a date and place of issue and this was maintained on the white notes until they were discontinued in 1956.

Notes were not, however, necessarily issued in the year that they were dated. This is true of the 1945 and 1947 issues and was the result of stockpiling to meet anticipated extra demand, at Christmas for example, which did not always materialise.

In 1970, the new Pictorial Series D £20 note was actually issued after Mr. J. S. Fforde had ceased to be Chief Cashier, although it carried his signature. Fforde and Page £1, £5 and £10 were issued concurrently for several months and when Malcolm Gill took over from David Somerset in 1988 it was over a year before the stock of Somerset £20 notes was exhausted.

HOW TO GRADE CONDITION

Unlike postage stamps, which are usually collected only in perfect condition, banknotes are collectable in various stages of wear and tear. The aim of any collector must be to obtain the best specimens available. In the case of notes from 1900–1928 this means at least VF; from 1928–1939 they should be at least EF and thereafter (with a few exceptions) uncirculated. One problem is that notes which appear to the inexperienced eye to be perfect are slightly 'off'. The commonest reason is the habit of cashiers to count a new packet and cause a slight bend in one corner. Such notes are perfectly acceptable but should be graded 98% or 99%.

The basic conditions are:

UNC	uncirculated	100
EF	extremely fine	90
VF	very fine	75
F	fine	55
Fair		30

With 18th or 19th century notes it is unusual to find anything better than VF. Many can only be described as fair and some notes are rejoined due to the practice of sending the two halves by separate transport as a safeguard against theft.

Be careful to avoid laundered notes where dirt may be removed but wear cannot be disguised, giving the note a very artificial look. If you want to smarten up a dirty note, use a soft india rubber and under no circumstances resort to soaking, washing or bleaching. At best the value of the note will be substantially reduced; at worst it it will be irreparably damaged and become worthless to collectors.

There is no substitute for experience in grading. A good dealer can grade a note on sight without using a numerical system. The main points to check fall under five main headings:

CLEANLINESS, FOLDS, EDGES, SURFACE AND BODY

Most commonly you will find a fold and perhaps damage to one edge. Deduct five points for damage under each heading to ascertain the grade, so for example if a note is folded and has a small nick on the edge, it will be 90%. Dealers will normally mention ink or biro marks and handstamps (common on white notes) over and above the general grading. The price for a truly 100% uncirculated note will normally, but not invariably, be higher than the catalogue price for an EF example.

The policy in the catalogue is to avoid confusing collectors by quoting too many price differentials which might be unsustainable. The author and the publishers feel that it is in everyone's best interest for the EF/VF system to be maintained.

Appendix A—Serial Number Charts

Ten Shillings

Unthreaded Mahon (LNoNo)	Catterns (LNoNo)	Peppiatt (LNoNo)	Peppiatt (NoNoL)	Wartime Peppiatt (LNoNoL)	Threaded Peppiatt (NoNoL)	Beale (NoNoL)	Beale (LNoNoL)
A 01			01Z	Z 01D /Z 01E			Z - - Z
Z 01			- - Y	Y - - D /Y - - E			Y - - Z
Y - -	V 14		- - X	X - - D /X 21E			X - - Z
X - -	U - -		- - W	W - - D			W - - Z
W - -	T - -		- - U	U - - D			U - - Z
V 11	S - -		- - T	T - - D			T - - Z
	R - -		- - S	S - - D			S - - Z
	O - -		- - R	R - - D			R - - Z
	N - -		79O	O - - D			O - - Z
	M - -			N - - D			N - - Z
	L - -		Post-war	M - - D			M - - Z
	K 99		05L –71L	L - - D	71L		L - - Z
		J 01		K - - D	- - K		K - - Z
		H - -		J - - D	- - J		J - - Z
		E - -		H - - D	- - H		H - - Z
		D - -		E - - D	91E	92E	E - - Z
		C - -		D - - D		- - D	D 85Z
		B - -		C - - D		- - C	
		A 99		B - - D		99B	
				A 99D			
Replacement Notes					01A /03A	04A /35A	

O'Brien (LNoNoL)	O'Brien (LNoNoL)	Portrait O'Brien (LNoNo)	Hollom (LNoNo)	Hollom (NoNoL)	Fforde (NoNoL)	Fforde (LNoNoL)
	Z 01Y /Z 01X	A 01		01A		A 01N
	Y - - Y /Y 25X	B - -		- B		B - - N
	X - - Y	C - -		- C		C - - N
	W - - Y	D - -		- D		D 38N
	U - - Y	E - -		- E		
	T - - Y	H - -		- H		
	S - - Y	J - -		- J		
	R - - Y	K 64	K 65	- K		
	O - - Y		L - -	- L		
	N - - Y	M01/M18	M19/M55	Replacement Notes	Replacement Notes	M56/M80
	M - - Y		N - -	- N	26R	
	L - - Y		R - -	25R	- S	
	K - - Y		S - -		- T	
	J - - Y		T - -		- U	
	H - - Y		U - -		- W	
	E - - Y		W - -		- X	
D 86Z	D - - Y		X - -		- Y	
C - - Z	C - - Y		Y - -		99Z	
B - - Z	B - - Y		Z 99			
A 95Z	A 99Y		Replacement Notes			
	36A –68A	Replacement Notes				

One Pound

Unthreaded Mahon (LNoNo)	Catterns (LNoNo)	Catterns (NoNoL)	Peppiatt (NoNoL)	Unthreaded Peppiatt (LNoNoL)	Wartime Peppiatt (LNoNoL)	Wartime Peppiatt (LNoNoL)	Wartime Peppiatt (LNoNoL)
A 01		01A –99A		A03A	A01D	A01E	A01H
B - -			01B	B - -A	B - -D	B - -E	B - -H
C - -			- -C	C - -A	C - -D	C - -E	C - -H
D - -			- -D	D - -A	D - -D	D - -E	D - -H
E - -			- -E	E - -A	E - -D	E - -E	E - -H
F - -							
G - -							
H 31	H 33		- -H	H - -A	H - -D	H - -E	H - -H
	J - -		- -J	J - -A	J - -D	J - -E	J - -H
	K - -		- -K	K - -A	K - -D	K - -E	K - -H
	L - -		- -L	L 39A	L - -D	L - -E	L - -H
	M - -		- -M		M - -D	M - -E	M - -H
	N - -		- -N		N - -D	N - -E	N - -H
	O - -		- -O	Post-war	O - -D	O - -E	O - -H
	R - -		- -R	R01A	R - -D	R - -E	R - -H
	S - -		- -S	S48A	S - -D	S - -E	S - -H
	T - -		- -T	(overlaps to threaded)	T - -D	T - -E	T - -H
	U - -		- -U		U - -D	U - -E	U - -H
	W - -		- -W		W - -D	W38E	W - -H
	X - -		- -X		X - -D		X94H
	Y - -		- -Y		Y - -D		
	Z 99		99Z		Z87D		

Threaded							
Peppiatt (LNoNoL)	Peppiatt (LNoNoL)	Beale (LNoNoL)	Beale (LNoNoL)	Beale (LNoNoL)	O'Brien (LNoNoL)	O'Brien (LNoNoL)	O'Brien (LNoNoL)
	A01B		A 01C	A01J		A01K	A02L
	B - - B		B - - C	B - - J		B - - K	B - - L
	C - - B		C - - C	C - - J		C - - K	C - - L
	D - - B		D - - C	D - - J		D - - K	D - - L
			E - - C	E - - J		E - - K	E - - L
	H36B	H 37B	H - - C	H - - J		H - - K	H - - L
	H36B						
		J - - B	J - - C	J - - J		· J - - K	J - - L
		K - - B	K - - C	K - - J		K - - K	K13L
		L - - B	L - - C	L63J	L64J	L - - K	(series ends)
		M - - B	M - - C		M - - J	M - - K	
		N - - B	N - - C		N - - J	N - - K	
		O - - B	O - - C		O - - J	O - - K	
		R - - B	R - - C		R - - J	R - - K	
(overlaps)	Replacement Notes			Replacement Notes			Replacement Notes
S40A	S01S/S09S	S - - B	S - - C	S10S/S70S	S - - J	S - - K	S71S/S97S
T - - A	(to Beale)	T - - B	T - - C	(to O'Brien)	T - - J	T - - K	S01T/S21T
U - - A		U - - B	U - - C		U - - J	U - - K	
W - - A		W - - B	W - - C		W - - J	W - - K	
X - - A		X - - B	X - - C		X - - J	X - - K	
Y - - A		Y - - B	Y - - C		Y - - J	Y - - K	
Z99A		Z99B	Z99C		Z99J	Z99K	

One Pound (*continued*)

Portrait O'Brien (NoNoL)	O'Brien (LNoNo)	O'Brien (LNoNoL)	Hollom (LNoNoL)	Hollom (LNoNoL)	Hollom (LNoNoL)	Hollom (LNoNoL)	Fforde (LNoNoL)	Fforde (LNoNoL)
A 01	01A	A 01N/A 06N (R)	A 09N (G)	A 01S	A 01U	A 01X		A 01Z
B - -	- - B	B 01N/B 76N	B 77N	B - - S	B - - U	B - - X		B - - Z
C - -	- - C		C - - N	C - - S	C - - U	C - - X		C - - Z
D - -	- - D		D - - N	D - - S	D - - U	D - - X		D - - Z
E - -	- - E		E - - N	E - - S	E - - U	E - - X		E - - Z
H - -	- - H		H - - N	H - - S	H - - U	H - - X		H - - Z
J - -	- - J		J - - N	J - - S	J - - U	J - - X		J - - Z
K - -	- - K		K - - N	K - - S	K - - U	K - - X		K - - Z (G)
L - -	- - L		L - - N	L - - S	L - - U	L - - X (G)		L 99Z
	M01/M68	Replacement Notes	M68/M99	01M/99M	M01N/M28N (G) / M01R/M08R	Links to Fforde	Links to Fforde	M29N/M42N (G) / M09R/M49R
N - -			A - - R	A - - T	A - - W	A 01Y		
R - -			B - - R	B - - T	B - - W	B 11Y	B 12Y	
S - -			C - - R	C - - T	C - - W (G)		C - - Y	
T - -			D - - R	D - - T (G)	D - - W		D - - Y	
U - -			E - - R	E - - T	E - - W		E - - Y (G)	
W - -			H - - R	H - - T	H - - W		H - - Y	
X - -			J - - R	J - - T	J - - W		J - - Y	
Y - -			K - - R	K - - T	K - - W		K - - Y	
Z 99			L - - R	L - - T	L - - W		L - - Y	

Fforde	Fforde	Fforde	Fforde	Page	Page	Page	Page
N01A	S 01A	U 01A			U - - A	X 01A	Z 01A
N - - B	S - - B	U - - B	X - - B		U - - B	X - - B	Z - - B
N - - C	S - - C	U - - C	X42C		U - - C	X - - C	Z - - C
N - - D	S - - D	U - - D			U - - D	X - - D	Z - - D
N - - E	S - - E	U - - E (G)				X - - E	Z - - E
N - - H	S - - H	U - - H		S87L	U - - H	X - - H	Z - - H
N - - J	S - - J					X - - J	Z - - J
N - - K	S - - K					X - - K	Z - - K
N - - L	S - - L					X - - L	Z - - L

Replacement Notes

Fforde	Fforde	Fforde	Page	Page	Page
N01M/N14M(G) R01M/R53M	S01M/S72M T01M/T04M	T29M/T32M(G) U01M		R44M/R99M S35M/S95M	W01M/W81M X01M/X60M
R - - A	T - - A	W01A		W - - A	Y 01A
R - - B (G)	T - - B	W - - B	T - - B	W - - B	Y - - B
R - - C	T - - C	W - - B		W - - C	Y - - C
R - - D	T - - D		T - - D	W - - D	Y - - D
R - - E	T - - E		T - - E	W - - E	Y - - E
R - - H	T - - H		T - - H	W - - H	Y - - H
R - - J	T - - J				Y - - J
R - - K	T - - K		T - - K		Y - - K
R - - L (G)	T - - L		T - - L		Y - - L

One Pound (*continued*)

Portrait Page (LLNoNo)	Page (LLNoNo)	Page (LLNoNo)	Pictorial Page (LNoNo)	Page (NoNoL)	Page (LNoNoL)	Somerset (LLNoNo)	Somerset (LNoNoL)
A N01	C N01	E N01	A 01	01A	A 01N	A N01	C N01
A R--	C R--	E R--	B--	--B	B--N	A R--	C R--
A S--	C S--	E S--	C--	--C	C--N	A S--	C S--
A T--	C T--	E T--	D--	--D	D--N	A T--	C T--
A U--	C U--	E U--	E--	--E	E 80N	A U--	C U--
A W--	C W--	E W--	H--	--H		A W--	C W--
A X--	C X--	E X--	J--	--J		A X--	C X--
A Y--	C Y--	E Y--	K--	--K		A Y--	C Y--
A Z--	C Z--	E Z--	L--	--L		A Z--	C Z--
MR 01/MR 48	MT 01/MT 21	MW01/MW19	M01 (only)		Replacements		MN04/MN18
MS01/MS84	MU01/MU18						
B N--	D N--	H N--	N--	--N		B N--	D N--
B R--	D R--	H R--	R--	--R		B R--	D R--
B S--	D S--	H S--	S--	--S		B S--	D S--
B T--	D T--	H T--	T--	--T		B T--	D T--
B U--	D U--	H U--	U--	--U		B U--	D U--
B W--	D W--	H W--	W--	--W		B W--	D W--
B X--	D X--	H X--	X--	--X		B X--	D X--
B Y--	D Y--	H Y--	Y--	--Y		B Y--	D X--
B Z--	D Z--	H Z 62	Z 80	81Z (only)		B Z--	D Y 21
		(series ends)					(last £1)

Five Pounds

Britannia O'Brien (LNoNo)	O'Brien (LNoNo)	Portrait Hollom (LNoNo)	Fforde (LNoNo)	Fforde (NoNoL)	Page (NoNoL)	Pictorial Page (LNoNo)	Page (NoNoL)
A 01		A 01		01A		A 01	01A
B - -		B - -		- - B		B - -	- - B
C - -		C - -		- - C	03C	C - -	- - C
D - -		D - -		- - D	- - D	D - -	- - D
E 06		E - -		- - E	- - E	E - -	- - E
	H 01	H - -		- - H	- - H	H - -	- - H
	J - -	J - -		- - J	- - J	J - -	- - J
	K 45	K - -		- - K	- - K	K - -	- - K
	(series ends)	L - -		40L	30L	L 94	- - L
Replacement Notes		M01/M07	M08/M38	01M/15M	04M/10M	M01/M05	01M/08M
		N - -	R 20				- - N
		R 16	S - -				- - R
			T - -				- - S
			U - -				- - T
			W - -				- - U
			X - -				- - W
			Y - -				- - X
			Z 99				- - Y
							83Z

Five Pounds (continued)

Pictorial Page (LLNoNo)	Page (LLNoNo)	Somerset (LLNoNo)	Somerset (LLNoNo)	Somerset (LLNoNo)	Somerset (LLNoNo)	Gill (LLNoNo)	Gill (LLNoNo)	Series E Gill (LLNoNo)
A N 01	C N 01	D N 01	H N --	K N --	N A --	R D 01	S A --	A 01
A R --	C R --	D R --	H R --	K R --	N B --	R E --	S B --	B --
A S --	C S --	D S --	H S --	K S --	N C 90	R H --	S C --	C --
A T --	C T --	D T --	H T --	K T --		R J --	S D --	D --
A U --	C U --	D U --	H U --	K U --		R K --	S E 90	(cont.)
A W --	C W --	D W --	H W --	K W --		R L --	(series ends)	
A X --	C X --	D X --	H X --	K X --				
A Y --		D Y --	H Y --	K Y --				
A Z --		D Z --	H Z --	K Z --				

Somerset OCR notes found with AN91--BR91--CS91--DT91--EU91--HW91--JX91--KY91--LZ91

Pictorial Page (LLNoNo)	Page (LLNoNo)	Somerset (LLNoNo)	Somerset (LLNoNo)	Somerset (LLNoNo)	Somerset (wide thread) (LLNoNo)
B N --		E N --	J N --	L N --	R A 01
B R --		E R --	J R --	L R --	R B --
B S --		E S --	J S --	L S --	R C 90
B T --		E T --	J T --	L T --	
B U --		E U --	J U --	L U --	
B W --		E W --	J W --	L W --	
B X --		E X --	J X --	L X --	
B Y --		E Y --	J Y --	L Y --	
B Z --	E Z 52/E Z 56	E Z 90	J Z --	L Z 90	

Ten Pounds

Portrait Hollom (LNoNo)	Fforde (LNoNo)	Page (LNoNo)	Pictorial Page (LNoNo)	Somerset (LNoNo)	Somerset (NoNoL)	Somerset (LLNoNo)	Somerset (LLNoNo)	Gill (LLNoNo)	Gill (LLNoNo)
A 01/A 40	A 41/A 95	A 90	A 01		01A	A N01	C N--		E N--
	(overlaps)	B--	B--		--B	A R--	C R 90		E R--
		C--	C--		--C	A S--	C S 01 (New Thread)		E S--
		(series ends)	D--		--D	A T--	C T--		E T--
			E--		--E	A U--	C U--		E U--
			H--		--H	A W--	C W--		E W--
			J--		--J	A X--	C X--		(cont.)
			K--		--K	A Y--	C Y--		
			L--		40L	A Z--	C Z--		
M01(?)	M01	M01/M50	Replacement Notes						
			N--	U 01		B N--	D N 30		D R 01
			R--	W--		B R--			D S--
			S--	X--		B S--			D T--
			T--	Y--		B T--			D U--
			U 39	Z 80		B U--			D W--
						B W--			D X--
						B X--			D Y--
						B Y--			D Z--
						B Z--			

Twenty Pounds

Pictorial Fforde (LNoNo)	Page (LNoNo)	Somerset (LNoNo)	New Thread Somerset (NoNoL)	Gill (NoNoL)
A 01/A 05	A 06		01A	
	B --		-- B	
	C --		-- C	
	D 79		-- D	
		E 01	-- E	
		H --	-- H	
		J 40	-- J	
			40K	
				01L
M01	M01/M04	Replacement Notes		-- M
				-- N
				-- R
				(cont.)

Fifty Pounds

Somerset (LNoNo)	Gill (LNoNo)
A01	
B --	
	C --
	D --
	(cont.)

Appendix B—The White Notes

The one undeniable fact about the white notes is that the Bank of England devised an extraordinarily complex system of prefix coding which has taken years of patient research to unravel. Even now there are unexplained gaps and inconsistencies and short of gaining access to the Bank's ledgers or finding examples of every single note, the complete story may never be known.

Many collectors have put in countless hours of research and special mention should be made of IBNS members, Bob Blake (on whose year planner the white note charts are based) and Michael Brill, building on earlier work by Howard Lunn, Ernest Quarmby and Jim Coulthard. We owe them a debt of gratitude for their efforts.

It is not, however, possible within the space of this catalogue to list every single date and prefix, but it is hoped that those who are interested will be able to construct their own detailed charts of 20th century white £5 notes issued in London from J. G. Nairne onwards.

The basic formula rests on the distinction between years ending in even numbers (e.g. 1922) and those ending in odd numbers (e.g. 1933). Taking the London £5 first, in even years the Bank broadly speaking used the first half of the month, and in odd years the second half of the month. The balance of the days and dates available in each month were allocated to high denomination notes and branch issues. However, the Bank never used Sundays, Christmas Day or Good Friday.

This system seems to have been started with J. G. Nairne sometime about 1904, but the precise date has not yet been established. 19th century notes used a different random system and so far it has not been possible to pin it down with certainty.

As depression set in after the 1929 Wall Street crash, quite long gaps are apparent in the production runs due to the contraction in the money supply. There are also numbers unconfirmed by positive sighting of notes; it cannot necessarily be assumed because there was a prefix number allocated to a particular date, that notes were actually printed with that date.

NAIRNE FIVE POUNDS (from 1904)

Prefix coding: Numbers over letter

London issues: 1st–13th in even years; 18th–31st in odd years:

1904 'C' prefix from 28 to 99   (1 January to 7 July)
1904 'D' prefix from 1 to 61   (8 July to 13 December)
1905 'D' prefix from 62 to 99   (18 January to 26 April)
1905 'E' prefix from 1 to 92   (27 April to 30 December)
1906 'E' prefix from 93 to 99   (1 January to 8 January)
1906 'H' prefix from 1 to 99   (9 January to 8 October)
1906 'J' prefix from 1 to 27   (9 October to 13 December)
1907 'J' prefix from 28 to 99   (18 January to 25 July)

1907 (26 July) *Prefix coding:* Letter over numbers

1907 'A' prefix from 1 to 58   (26 July to 28 December)
   (it appears that 30 December was not used in 1907)
1908 'A' prefix from 59 to 99   (1 January to 9 April)
1908 'B' prefix from 1 to 57   (10 April to 10 September)
   (unrecorded numbers plus gap of about two months)

1909 'B' prefix from 98 to 99   (25 March to 26 March)
1909 'C' prefix from 1 to 99   (27 March to 27 December)
1909 'D' prefix from 1 to 4   (28 December to 31 December)
1910 'D' prefix from 5 to 99   (1 January to 7 September)
1910 'E' prefix from 1 to 38   (8 September to 13 December)
1911 'E' prefix from 39 to 99   (18 January to 27 June)
1911 'H' prefix from 1 to 70   (28 June to 30 December)
1912 'H' prefix from 71 to 99   (1 January to 7 March)
1912 'J' prefix from 1 to 99   (8 March to 6 December)

1912 (7 December) *Prefix coding:* Numbers over letter

1912 'A' prefix from 1 to 6   (7 December to 13 December)
1913 'A' prefix from 7 to 99   (18 January to 24 September)
1913 'B' prefix from 1 to 37   (25 September to 30 December)
1914 'B' prefix from 38 to 99   (1 January to 9 June)
1914 'C' prefix from 1 to 70   (10 June to 12 December)
1915 'C' prefix from 71 to 99   (18 January to 26 March)
1915 'D' prefix from 1 to 77   (27 March to 26 October)
   (gap of about two months)

1916 'D' prefix from 78 to 99   (1 January to 12 February)
1916 'E' prefix from 1 to 11   (1 March to 13 March)
1917 No issues

HARVEY FIVE POUNDS (from 1918)

Prefix coding: Numbers over letter

London issues: 1st–14th in even years; 18th–30th/31st in odd years:

1918 'E' prefix from	12	to	99	(10 May to 14 December)
1919 'H' prefix from	1	to	99	(18 January to 26 September)
1919 'J' prefix from	1	to	37	(27 September to 31 December)
1920 'J' prefix from	38	to	99	(1 January to 5 May)

HARVEY FIVE POUNDS (from 1920)

Prefix coding: Letter over numbers

London issues: 1st–17th in even years; 18th–30th/31st in odd years:

1920 'A' prefix from	1	to	99	(6 May to 1 December)
1920 'B' prefix from	1	to	14	(2 December to 17 December)
1921 'B' prefix from	15	to	99	(18 January to 24 August)
1921 'C' prefix from	1	to	48	(25 August to 27 December)

(There are no confirmed sightings from 28 December–12 February)

1922 'C' prefix from	76	to	99	(13 February to 5 April)
1922 'D' prefix from	1	to	72	(6 April to 6 September)

Prefix coding: 3 numbers over letter

1922 'D' prefix from	101	to	152	(7 September to 16 December)
1923 'D' prefix from	153	to	288	(18 January to 31 December)
1924 'D' prefix from	289	to	399	(1 January to 11 August)
1924 'E' prefix from	001	to	064	(12 August to 17 December)
1925 'E' prefix from	065	to	098	(19 January to 31 March)

MAHON FIVE POUNDS (from 1925)

Prefix coding: 3 numbers over letter

1925 'E' prefix from	099	to	201	(1 April to 31 December)
1926 'E' prefix from	202	to	376	(1 January to 17 December)
1927 'E' prefix from	377	to	399	(18 January to 19 March)
1927 'H' prefix from	001	to	115	(21 March to 31 December)
1928 'H' prefix from	116	to	146	(2 January to 2 March)

(unrecorded numbers plus gap of about two months)

1928 'H' prefix from	153	to	189	(3 May to 12 July)

(gap of about eight months)

CATTERNS FIVE POUNDS (from 1929)

Prefix coding: 3 numbers over letter

1929 'H' prefix from 201 to 305 (30 March to 31 December)
1930 'H' prefix from 306 to 399 (1 January to 8 July)
1930 'J ' prefix from 001 to 022 (9 July to 16 August)
(unrecorded numbers plus gap of about five months)

1931 'J ' prefix from 044 to 135 (23 January to 22 September)
(gap of about three months)

1932 'J ' prefix from 136 to 238 (1 January to 2 August)
(unrecorded numbers plus gap of about six months)

1933 'J ' prefix from 262 to 315 (25 February to 22 July)
(unrecorded numbers plus gap of about five months)

1934 'J ' prefix from 328 to 351 (1 January to 10 February)
(unrecorded numbers plus gap of about three months)

PEPPIATT FIVE POUNDS (from 1934)

Prefix coding: 3 numbers over letter

1934 'J ' prefix from 357 to 399 (7 May to 6 August)

1924 (7 August) *Prefix coding:* Letter over 3 numbers

1934 'A' prefix from 100 to 135 (7 August to 13 October)
(gap of about three months)

1935 'A' prefix from 136 to 255 (18 January to 23 November)
(gap of about one month)

1936 'A' prefix from 256 to 352 (1 January to 13 July)
(unrecorded numbers plus gap of about seven months)

1937 'A' prefix from 374 to 399 (24 February to 30 April)
1937 'B' prefix from 100 to 144 (18 May to 28 August)
(unrecorded numbers plus gap of about six months)

1938: London issues: 1st–16th in even years; 19th–30th/31st in odd years:

1938 'B' prefix from 191 to 320 (9 March to 16 December)
1939 'B' prefix from 321 to 383 (19 January to 19 July)
(unrecorded numbers plus gap of about five months)

1940 'B' prefix from 386 to 390 (1 January to 5 January)
(unrecorded numbers plus gap of about ten months)

1940 'B' prefix from 397 to 399 (4 November to 6 November)
1940 'C' prefix from 100 to 112 (7 November to 6 December)
(unrecorded numbers plus gap of about four days)

PEPPIATT – Five Pounds (from 1934) (contd.)

1941 'C' prefix from 118 to 143 (20 January to 20 March)
(unrecorded numbers plus gap of about three months)

1941 'C' prefix from 170 to 196 (25 August to 24 October)
(unrecorded numbers plus gap of about two months)

1942 'C' prefix from 204 to 306 (7 January to 8 September)
(gap of about three months)

1943 'C' prefix from 307 to 397 (16 January to 31 July)

1943 (1 August) London issues use the whole of the month from now on:

1943 'C' prefix from 398 to 399 (1 August to 3 August)
1943 'D' prefix from 073 to 160 (4 August to 13 November)
(gap of just over a month)

1944 'D' prefix from 161 to 238 (1 January to 31 March)
(gap of about two months)

1944 'D' prefix from 239 to 318 (1 June to 1 September)

PEPPIATT FIVE POUNDS (from 1944)

1944 (2 September)   Threaded paper introduced
                    Prefix coding: Letter, number, number

1944 E 01 (2 September)   to   E 99 (27 December)
1944 H 01 (28 December)   to   H 03 (30 December)
1945 H 04 (1 January)   to   H 99 (23 April)
1945 J 01 (24 April)   to   J 99 (16 August)
1945 K 01 (17 August)   to   L 99 (10 December)
1945 L 01 (11 December)   to   L 02 (12 December)
1946 No issues

1947 (1 January)   Thinner threaded paper
                    Prefix coding: Letter, number, number

1947 L 03 (1 January)   to   L 99 (24 April 1947)
1947 M01 (25 April)   to   M71 (16 July 1947)
1948 No issues

BEALE FIVE POUNDS   (from 1949)

Prefix coding: Letter, number, number

1949 M72 (1 March)	to	M99 (1 April)
1949 N 01 (2 April)	to	N 99 (27 July)
1949 O 01 (28 July)	to	O 99 (19 November)
1949 P 01 (21 November)	to	P 36 (31 December)
1950 P 37 (2 January)	to	P 99 (15 March)
1950 R 01 (16 March)	to	R 99 (10 July)
1950 S 01 (11 July)	to	S 99 (2 November)
1950 T 01 (3 November)	to	T 49 (30 December)
1951 T 50 (1 January)	to	T 99 (27 February)
1951 U 01 (28 February)	to	U 99 (23 June)
1951 V 01 (25 June)	to	V 99 (17 October)
1951 W01 (18 October)	to	W63 (31 December)
1952 W64 (1 January)	to	W99 (11 February)
1952 X 01 (12 February)	to	X 99 (6 June)
1952 Y 01 (7 June)	to	Y 70 (27 August)

(gap of two years four months)

O'BRIEN FIVE POUNDS   (from 1955)

Prefix coding: Letter, number, number

1955 Y 71 (17 January)	to	Y 99 (18 February)
1955 Z 01 (19 February)	to	Z 99 (15 June)

Prefix coding: Letter, number, number, letter

1955 A 01A (16 June)	to	A 99A (8 October)
1955 B 01A (10 October)	to	B 72A (31 December)
1956 B 73A (2 January)	to	B 99A (1 February)
1956 C 01A (2 February)	to	C 99A (28 May)
1956 D 01A (29 May)	to	D 99A (20 September)

White £5 notes without metal thread were legal tender until 1 March 1946.
White £5 notes with metal thread were legal tender until 13 March 1961.

HIGH DENOMINATION AND BRANCH NOTES

All the high denomination notes and £5 notes from the various branches carried dates during each year not taken by the London £5 and used the rest of the letters in the alphabet K to Z.

Because of the relative scarcity of some notes conclusions are difficult at the present time, but research is continuing and the following brief summary may help those interested in pursuing the subject.

FIVE POUNDS Branch notes:

$\frac{T}{--}$ to $\frac{T}{81}$ (19- - to 1909) $\frac{U}{36}$ to $\frac{V}{53}$ (1910 to 1911)

$\frac{21}{T}$ to $\frac{99}{T}$ (1913 to 1916) $\frac{01}{U}$ to $\frac{99}{U}$ (1916 to 1919)

$\frac{T}{01}$ to $\frac{T}{99}$ (1919 to 1920) $\frac{U}{01}$ to $\frac{U}{99}$ (1920 to 1922)

$\frac{101}{U}$ to $\frac{483}{U}$ (1921 to 1931) $\frac{T}{101}$ to $\frac{T}{280}$ (1931 to 1938)

TEN POUNDS London

$\frac{01}{K}$ to $\frac{99}{K}$ (1914 to 1920) $\frac{01}{L}$ to $\frac{199}{L}$ (1921 to 1931)

$\frac{K}{101}$ to $\frac{K}{199}$ (1932 to 1938) $\frac{L}{101}$ to $\frac{L}{138}$ (1938 to 1942)

TEN POUNDS Branch

$\frac{V}{--}$ to $\frac{V}{44}$ (19- - to 1911) $\frac{28}{V}$ to $\frac{170}{V}$ (1918 to 1938)

TWENTY POUNDS London   TWENTY POUNDS Branch

$\frac{M}{--}$ to $\frac{M}{--}$ (19- - to 19- -) $\frac{W}{8}$ to $\frac{W}{16}$ (1910 to 1913)

$\frac{17}{M}$ to $\frac{57}{M}$ (1918 to 1938) $\frac{17}{W}$ to $\frac{62}{W}$ (1918 to 1937)

FIFTY POUNDS London

$\frac{N}{--}$ to $\frac{N}{--}$ (19-- to 19--)

$\frac{11}{N}$ to $\frac{67}{N}$ (1918 to 1941)

FIFTY POUNDS Branch

$\frac{X}{--}$ to $\frac{X}{16}$ (19-- to 1911)

$\frac{2}{X}$ to $\frac{76}{X}$ (1913 to 1934)

ONE HUNDRED POUNDS London

$\frac{O}{--}$ to $\frac{O}{--}$ (19-- to 1912)

$\frac{1}{O}$ to $\frac{58}{O}$ (1913 to 1938)

ONE HUNDRED POUNDS Branch

$\frac{--}{--}$ to $\frac{Y}{27}$ (19-- to 1911)

$\frac{5}{Y}$ to $\frac{96}{Y}$ (1913 to 1936)

FIVE HUNDRED POUNDS London

$\frac{05}{R}$ to $\frac{--}{\_}$ (1925 to 19--)

FIVE HUNDRED POUNDS Branch

$\frac{--}{\_}$ to $\frac{43}{Z}$ (19-- to 1936)

ONE THOUSAND POUNDS London only

$\frac{05}{S}$ to $\frac{14}{S}$ (1925 to 1938)

Branch notes in the 20th century were issued from:

BIRMINGHAM	MANCHESTER
BRISTOL	NEWCASTLE
HULL	PLYMOUTH
LEEDS	PORTSMOUTH
LIVERPOOL	(closed 30 April 1914)

Collectors may find it useful to know the number of white notes which, according to Bank of England reports, were outstanding at particular dates:

	1939	1950	1956	1963	1968
£5	7,656,600	24,123,600	48,419,400	—	—
£10	1,459,600	113,900	65,200	40,000	—
£20	221,800	25,500	14,950	9,250	7,800
£50	246,100	21,380	11,840	7,140	5,540
£100	265,180	21,130	10,540	6,280	4,910
£500	7,308	608	240	104	78
£1,000	23,119	386	122	74	63

Selected Bibliography

As Good As Gold—300 Years of British Bank Note Design by V. H. Hewitt and J. M. Keyworth. Published 1987 by British Museum Publications in association with the Bank of England.

The Moneymakers International by W. Kranister. Published 1989 by Black Bear Publishing, Cambridge.

Bank of England and Treasury Notes 1694–1970 by D. M. Miller. Published 1970 by Corbitt and Hunter Ltd. (Minerva Numismatic Handbooks No. 6).

A Guide to Collecting England Banknotes by David Bevan. Published 1970 by Larson Publications.

Money in Britain: A History of the Coins and Notes of the British Isles by C. R. Josset. Published 1971 by David and Charles.

Money: From Cowrie Shells to Credit Cards edited by Joe Cribb. Published 1986 by British Museum Publications.

The Bank of England Note by A. D. Mackenzie. Published 1953 by the Cambridge University Press.

The Currency of the Great War by Benjamin White. Published 1921 by Waterlow and Sons.

Nazi Counterfeiting of British Currency during World War II: Operation Andrew and Operation Bernhard by Bryan Burke. Published 1987 by The Book Shop, 727 West Highland Avenue, San Bernardino, California 92405, U.S.A.

A great many general histories have been written about the Bank of England including:

Inside the Bank of England by Philip Geddes. Published 1987 by Boxtree Ltd.

The Bank of England 1891–1944 by R. S. Sayers. Published 1976 by the Cambridge University Press (two volumes).

The Bank of England: A History by Sir John Clapham. Published 1944 by the Cambridge University Press (two volumes).

The Bank of England From Within by W. Marston Acres. Published 1931 by the Oxford University Press (two volumes).

Bibliography of the Bank of England by T. A. Stephens. Published by Effingham Wilson & Co., London 1897. Reprinted by Augustus M. Kelley, New York 1968.

Two magazines which specialise in banknotes are: *Bond and Banknote News* (Token Publishing, 84 High Street, Honiton, Devon EX14 8JW) and in America: *Banknote Reporter*.

Many interesting articles appear in the quarterly journal of the International Bank Note Society (IBNS). Full membership details can be obtained from the Assistant General Secretary: Suresh Gupta, 11 Middle Row, Kensington, London W10 5AT.